Penguin Book

UNDERSTANDING DEPRESSION

Maria Prendergast is a freelance writer and broadcaster. She has written many books, including *Understanding Asthma*, *Understanding Migraine*, *Stroke and Heart Attack Rehabilitation* and *Banks Behaving Badly*. She was a feature writer for Australian Consolidated Press for many years and currently contributes to newspapers in Australia and the United Kingdom. She is on a number of boards and committees, including the board of DepressioNet, and has a strong interest in social and environmental issues.

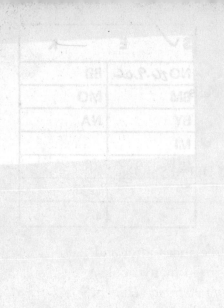

Understanding Depression

MARIA PRENDERGAST

With a foreword by Professor George Fink,
Director, Mental Health Research Institute of Victoria

PENGUIN BOOKS

PENGUIN BOOKS

Published by the Penguin Group
Penguin Group (Australia)
250 Camberwell Road, Camberwell, Victoria 3124, Australia
(a division of Pearson Australia Group Pty Ltd)
Penguin Group (USA) Inc.
375 Hudson Street, New York, New York 10014, USA
Penguin Group (Canada)
90 Eglinton Avenue East, Suite 700, Toronto ON M4P 2Y3, Canada
(a division of Pearson Penguin Canada Inc.)
Penguin Books Ltd
80 Strand, London WC2R 0RL, England
Penguin Ireland
25 St Stephen's Green, Dublin 2, Ireland
(a division of Penguin Books Ltd)
Penguin Books India Pvt Ltd
11 Community Centre, Panchsheel Park, New Delhi – 110 017, India
Penguin Group (NZ)
Cnr Airborne and Rosedale Roads, Albany, Auckland, New Zealand
(a division of Pearson New Zealand Ltd)
Penguin Books (South Africa) (Pty) Ltd
24 Sturdee Avenue, Rosebank, Johannesburg 2196, South Africa

Penguin Books Ltd, Registered Offices: 80 Strand, London WC2R 0RL, England

First published by Penguin Group (Australia), a division of Pearson Australia Group Pty Ltd, 2006

10 9 8 7 6 5 4 3 2 1

Text copyright © Maria Prendergast 2006

The moral right of the author has been asserted

Cover design by Janine Blackstock © Penguin Group (Australia)
Text design by George Dale © Penguin Group (Australia)
Typeset in Palatino 11.5/15pt by Midland Typesetters, Australia
Printed and bound in Australia by McPherson's Printing Group, Maryborough, Victoria

National Library of Australia
Cataloguing-in-Publication data:

Prendergast, Maria.
Understanding depression.
Bibliography.
Includes index.
ISBN 0 14 100493 2.
1. Depression, Mental – Popular works. 2. Depressed persons – Biography.
3. Depressed persons – Family relationships. I. Title.

362.25

www.penguin.com.au

FOR JOHN

CONTENTS

FOREWORD

My personal interest in mental disorder was primed by my chosen discipline, neuroendocrinology – the study of brain–hormone interactions – and heightened by a salutary experience with my first and probably best postgraduate student at Oxford University, Mukundan Sankar Aiyer. An incredibly bright, articulate and erudite man, with a formidable sense of humour and a huge infectious laugh, Mukund had everything going for him, or so it seemed. Dux and Captain of Cricket at India's famous Doon School, Mukund joined my lab as a Rhodes scholar. For three years we had enormous fun working at science 24/7, punctuated by pints at the Eagle and Child (where Tolkien had conceived of *The Hobbit* and *The Lord of the Rings*). Stunningly, having submitted a superb thesis for the degree of Doctor of Philosophy and just received news of a postdoctoral fellowship, Mukund, without warning and in the absence of any obvious external trigger, tripped into a most severe depression.

From being an active and productive young scientist, with a career for which there seemed to be no horizon, Mukund just sat at a bench, polishing it with a piece of gauze or, worse still, had the most terrifying fears and delusions. After several months of intense nursing Mukund's depression lifted as quickly and as mysteriously as it had come. He subsequently completed two years of postdoctoral research at a top lab in Virginia, and moved on to a position at the University of California in Los Angeles. There he received notification of appointment to a faculty position at the Indian Institute of Science at Bangalore. A chance to establish his own laboratory at the prestigious Bangalore Institute had been

Mukund's dream, and his letters to me confirmed that this ambition had not diminished. Alas, just a few weeks before his departure for Bangalore, news came that Mukund had committed suicide. He left a note to say that he could not face a life of recurring cycles of depression. The illness had returned to snuff out a beautiful mind and formidable intellect that was destined to make major breakthroughs in biomedicine.

Major depression, necessitating formal psychiatric treatment, affects about 20 per cent of people for varying lengths of time. The illness is devastating for the patient as well as for their families and carers, if indeed they have any. The socioeconomic burden of depression runs into several billions of dollars per annum. But this book is not about statistics. Rather it is an insightful compendium on the nature, diagnosis, treatment and outcome of depression that is easy to read and will be readily understood by the layperson. The book's strength lies in the ruthless honesty of the author and in the fact that all the points made are buttressed by one or more case histories. The case histories are remarkable for their variety and depth, providing a wide spectrum of experiences with which readers of differing backgrounds (whether patient or carer) can resonate. While this book is no cure for depression, it improves significantly our understanding of the illness and provides pointers towards the management of depression that might help prevent tragedies of the type that I recount above.

I applaud Maria Prendergast for her work, and strongly commend the book to persons who have or think that they might suffer from depression, and their carers. For others who may be interested in better understanding the impact of depression on those around them, this book provides a unique insight into the illness, often from a personal perspective.

Professor George Fink,

MB, BS, MD, DPHIL, FRCPE, FRSE, FRSA,

Director of the Mental Health Research Institute of Victoria

INTRODUCTION

When you've got it, if there were a magic wand across the room on the table that would make you happy and give you everything you want, it would be too much trouble to cross the room and pick it up!

> Dick Cavett, broadcaster, actor, author
> and a depression sufferer

It wrecks your life. It is like an awful, heavy, lead bubble in the head that won't let you think or feel. You have to declare war on it. You must constantly tell yourself not to give in. It saturates your whole being. It is a seamless, deep, deep sense of unbelievable pain dominating your sense of past, present and future.

> Helen Long, recovered depression sufferer

I have written this book for the non-medical person who wants to know more about the mood disorder known as depression. I want to stress that depression is not a character flaw or a sign of weakness; it is a genuine illness and should be recognised as such. Most of us have times when we experience a depressed or low mood. This is quite normal and does not generally interfere with everyday life in a significant way. These low moods can last from a few minutes to a few weeks and may be accompanied by irritability, negativity, pessimism, fatigue and lack of self-worth. These feelings can vary in severity but most people are still able to get on with their lives. Though it can be an unpleasant experience, a normal low mood is not usually all-consuming, and it does not cause the problems and disruption associated with true clinical depression.

Clinical depression is a world apart from low moods or transitory periods of negative thinking. It is vastly different to feeling sad or low. The pain of true depression can be unbearable if left untreated. As William Styron so eloquently says in his book *Darkness Visible,* 'depression remains nearly incomprehensible to those who have not experienced it in its extreme mode'.

In the course of my research I spoke with many psychologists, psychiatrists, general practitioners, health workers, and some hundreds of people who had suffered depression or cared for a depressed person. They all had strong and sometimes divergent opinions on how best to identify, cope with, live with and overcome depression. These views were founded on a mixture of medical and academic knowledge, personal and professional experience and personal perceptions. Some of the people I spoke with believed they had recovered, others continued to suffer but were determined to try and beat their illness. Others feared they would have to cope with depression for life.

Depression is not an illness that is simple to define. People's experiences and symptoms can be extremely diverse, as illustrated by their personal stories. Yet the individual contributions in this book reinforce the opinions of health practitioners who deal with depression, that with the correct treatment and support, it can be largely overcome or at the very least contained. Unlike some illnesses, depression is a condition where recovery or remission is a realistic goal. Sadly, it must be acknowledged that there is a small minority for whom current treatments provide little or no relief. These are the people who have what is termed 'treatment-resistant depression'. For these people the suffering and disability can be ongoing and long-term.

There was a difficult time during the creation of this book when I was uncertain about what angle or direction to take. Depression is a very complicated illness and I was aware that it was important not to become too technical and thus take the book beyond the scope of understanding of the non-medical reader.

I was swamped with information (and misinformation) and had a huge amount of material to absorb. I read books about depression written by doctors, psychologists and other health professionals. Many were informative and helpful but from my point of view the voices of depression sufferers and those who care for them were not heard. There is still much to learn about this disease, particularly its chemistry, and it was not my intention to undermine the role of the health profession in furthering our understanding of depression.

After several interviews I realised that I, too, was not really helping people to convey the 'feeling' of depression, but was focusing on explaining the 'state' of depression. I had not been asking the questions that would enable sufferers to fully express themselves. I found myself questioning if yet another book about depression was going to add to the wealth of practical information already available.

I was very close to abandoning the book when I received a phone call from a woman whose husband suffered from severe depression. She was quite desperate about her situation and needed help in her role as his main support. She had just returned from a futile search of bookshops, looking for a book that would offer guidance. She was not depressed, but depression was making her life a misery. She said to me:

> I feel so alone. There are no books that 'humanise' the experience of being depressed or living with someone who is depressed. Has any author ever asked a depressed person to explain exactly how they feel or what they would like to read about depression? Has anyone caring for a depressed person ever been given a real voice in any book?

Following that phone call I decided I would continue with the book. It was the words 'humanise the experience of depression' that made me realise I needed to listen with an open mind and heart to the people who really understood the pain and disruption caused by this illness, and who could also talk about their experience of treatment and recovery.

These were the people I sought out, and I have devoted a large section of the book to their individual, first-hand accounts. The people I interviewed varied widely in age, background and their experience of depression. Many gave permission for their real names to be used. Others requested that I use a pseudonym to protect family members, particularly children, from knowing about their battle, to avoid potential employment problems, or simply to respect their privacy. I agreed to their request because I do not believe the authority and power of their stories are diminished by their wish to remain anonymous in print.

I have been deeply moved by the experience of meeting so many people whose lives have been affected by depression. These include not only those who have the illness but those who live or work with a person suffering depression, and who are always there for them.

I hope that the honesty and courage of the individuals who have contributed to this book will inspire insight, understanding and compassion for this pervasive illness. Individuals suffering from any type of depression need the support of an enlightened society, not the judgement that comes from misunderstanding and ignorance.

The more we learn about a disease or disorder the more we are empowered to deal with it. The stories in this book are as inspirational as any adventurer's tale, or that of any well-known writer, artist, scientist or musician (and there are many) who fought and overcame depression in their life.

CHAPTER ONE

A PERVASIVE ILLNESS

Depression is widespread in the western world and becoming more so in many parts of the developing world. It has become a major health issue in Australia where it is currently estimated that over six million working days are lost each year to depression. For an illness that is nearly always treatable, depression causes enormous suffering and loss of productivity in the community.

Statistics show that more women than men suffer from depression and anxiety. However, some doctors believe that this difference between the sexes may be attributable to the fact that more women than men seek help for their illness.

> Many men won't go to a doctor, even when they are feeling terrible. Women tend to seek help and talk about how they feel more readily than men. I'm not convinced the perceived gender imbalance is real.
>
> GP, rural Victoria

People of all ages can experience depression. Children as young as five years old have been diagnosed, and depression is one of the most common mental health disorders in older people.

> Once diagnosed, old people can respond well to therapy and antidepressants. In my practice I have found that many old people are reluctant to admit that they are depressed, as they don't want to worry their families or add another illness to what they may already have. Ageing does present problems

for many people, but those problems can be dealt with and put in a more positive perspective if people are emotionally well. I have referred patients in their eighties to psychiatrists or therapists for depression treatment and the results have been good.

GP, Melbourne

One in five Australians will experience clinical depression at least once in their life and 4 per cent of the population will suffer from clinical depression in any one year. These figures include only those who have been diagnosed with depression by a doctor or other health professional and do not include those who do not seek help for their illness. At least ten million prescriptions are written in this country each year for antidepressants. People with untreated mental disorders, particularly depression, commit the majority of suicides in Australia. More than 200 Australians take their own lives in depression-related suicides each month and, tragically, Australia has one of the highest youth suicide rates in the world.

It is not uncommon for people to use drugs and alcohol to cope with depression. Alcohol abuse, in particular, is higher among depressed men than depressed women. Unfortunately, drugs can only ever provide a temporary escape from depressive symptoms, and in some cases can exacerbate the illness.

My brother committed suicide a few months ago. He was depressed, and his depressed moods were worse when he used marijuana. It was obvious to all of us who loved him that he was worse after smoking joints but he had become emotionally addicted to marijuana. He developed schizo-phrenia over the last year of his life. Our GP was extremely concerned about the marijuana smoking because she is convinced it can trigger destructive emotional responses and, for some people, mental illness. If people only knew the damage marijuana can cause. The wonderful priest who conducted his funeral at our local church understands the problems such people suffer, much more than any psychiatrist or any social worker that my brother saw. Substance abuse, depression and other mental illnesses among young people are huge.

Jasmine Clark, aged twenty-six

The World Health Organization (WHO) reports that depression is the fourth most significant cause of suffering and disability worldwide (behind heart disease, cancer and traffic accidents), and predicts that by 2020 it will be the leading cause of disability in the developed world.

The possibility of reversing this chilling trend will occur only if more people seek help for their depression, if health professionals develop better skills and techniques for detection and diagnosis, and if more money is made available for treatments and research.

There is a crisis in the availability and delivery of mental health services in Australia and this impacts directly on all mental illness including depression. Services are barely coping with the numbers of people suffering from acute episodes of illness, much less providing preventive advice, ongoing treatment and support. There are no coherent national strategies covering such issues as education and training for the family and other carers of people with mental illness, including depression. Much unnecessary suffering could be alleviated for thousands of people if more funding was allocated to meet the ever-increasing demand in the community.

A recent initiative of the Federal Government under Medicare Plus enables GPs to refer people with 'complex, chronic needs' to a psychologist, but the referral is limited to five sessions. This is clearly inadequate and excludes many depressed people who would benefit from such a service. If people were able to access assistance before their illness became 'chronic' the progression of their disease could well be prevented.

The measures required to properly treat depression are not cheap, and people on low incomes who are unable to afford private health insurance can face a long wait for an appointment with a public-funded psychologist or any allied professional. This situation does not bode well for our community as a whole, for the personal and social costs of depression are immeasurable, placing enormous strain on individuals and families. Politicians intent on cost-cutting would be well advised to reflect on the consequences facing our community if the specialised services required to treat all mental health problems are not provided.

The Australian Federal Government currently spends only 7 per cent of its health budget on mental health services compared to figures of up to 15 per cent in other developed countries. Fewer than one person in six with depression or anxiety who is dependent on the public health system receives care that meets international standards.

It is important that health professionals and the general public continue to agitate for further funding to help cope with the distressing lack of support for some of society's most vulnerable members.

Beds in the emergency departments of Australian hospitals are commonly occupied by people with mental health problems – there is nowhere else for them to go unless they can afford a private clinic. Sufferers and their families are sometimes desperate for support. Taking someone with mental health problems to an emergency department is not the first choice for preferred treatment, but unfortunately it is often the only option if a GP is unavailable or considers the circumstances too difficult to deal with. This situation is placing an unfair burden on emergency departments' medical staff, who are generally not trained or equipped to deal with mental illness, and does not provide the care and support so urgently required by the patient and their family.

Though depression seems to be constantly in the news, be it high-profile celebrities talking about their therapies or favourite clinics, or reports of medical breakthroughs in understanding the chemistry of the brain, contemporary society is not well educated or particularly sympathetic when it comes to understanding depression. There remains a stigma attached to depression. It can manifest in various ways such as jokes, discrimination and misunderstanding. Some people feel uneasy and even threatened when confronted with the subject of mental health. Unfortunately some people only superficially accept depression as a genuine illness.

In his book *Churchill's Black Dog*, Dr Anthony Storr writes about 'normal people' as opposed to 'depressed people'. Storr is a highly respected psychiatrist and writer in the UK, but this comment is unhelpful because it implies that people with depression are different from the rest of us. No one wants to be labelled because of an illness. We are all a lot more than our illness, be it asthma, diabetes or depression. People with depression already have the misfortune to be suffering from an illness that is still surrounded by misconceptions and myths. Life is made even harder for a person with depression if they are made to feel they are abnormal.

A widely quoted comment by Senator Helen Coonan in Parliament in 2002 reflects an attitude that contributes to the stigma surrounding depression:

> People who might be just malingering, if you like, or have an anxiety condition or depression ... They do really need to get over it and get back to work.

Coonan did apologise subsequently, but such comments can cause pain and give credence to the view that depression is some sort of character weakness. Comments like 'pull your socks up' or 'count your blessings' that are often directed towards a person with depression are ignorant and counterproductive, even when said with good intentions.

Is it the result of a terrible malaise in our society? So many people seem unhappy and discontented. You read about people working longer and longer hours and not having time to nurture personal relationships or engage in any leisure activities. Humans are not machines. We need to have a balanced life if we are to be mentally and physically well. I am really freaked by the increasing number of people coming into my surgery suffering from some type of depression or anxiety. And let me add that I work in an affluent suburb in Sydney, so money worries are not the reason that many of my patients are depressed. Sometimes I really don't know how to respond, particularly when so many patients obviously need help but are not prepared to admit the problem. I know a lot of my patients lie to me, even though they know they need help. Some become very defensive if I suggest that they may be feeling depressed or that depression may be a possible reason for their litany of physical complaints. It's a very, very difficult situation for a doctor when people are not prepared to be open about what is really troubling them. I find that men are much more reluctant to talk about their feelings than women. I have some male patients who would rather have an amputation than admit their real problem is feeling low or depressed.

GP, Sydney

Ideally we would all like to enjoy continuous healthy emotional function, but to maintain this state is much harder for some than for others.

It can be particularly galling for a depressed person to observe another person surviving a really hard time without becoming stressed out or developing depression. This tends to reinforce the view that depression is some sort of character flaw, and can lead to feelings of shame and guilt that exacerbate the sufferer's total negativity and despair.

Identifying and removing some of the triggers for depression would involve many societal and economic changes that may well be impossible to implement in our lifetime. It is beyond the scope of this book to discuss in any detail the social, political and economic ills that contribute to so much misery, but factors such as family breakdown, job insecurity, financial stress, physical ill health and substance abuse all contribute to the high rate of depression in our society.

Sadly it has to be acknowledged that the circumstances of some people's lives are indescribably awful. In real life there is no good fairy to wave a wand and make everything all right. People who have suffered childhood abuse, have little education, no employment, no home, no family and no hope are part of our community and it is no wonder that some of them develop severe emotional problems. Some of these people may not have the money to buy this or any other book and may have to rely on inadequate health and social services as their only source of information, support and guidance.

At the same time there are depression sufferers who do have loving families, good education and jobs, have high standing in the community, and are financially secure. There are no external hardships or challenges that may explain 'feeling depressed', and this can result in additional guilt and feelings of being ungrateful or weak. 'I have everything I could want, so why do I feel this way?'

There definitely seems to be a link between mood disorders and creativity. Throughout history, many famous artists, writers and musicians have been diagnosed with depression or other mental illnesses. Their extreme moods and emotional journeys often caused great anguish and quite possibly fuelled their creativity.

Regardless of our circumstances we all have to accept that life can be a struggle on an almost daily basis. Life experiences exact a price. We all have to live, work, love and interact in an increasingly complex world. Currently the threats of terrorism, economic insecurity and environmental problems such as global warming and overpopulation have the potential to erode the emotional well-being of the most optimistic person. Sadly we are living in a society where there is much alienation, disconnection and isolation. Many people are struggling to find a purpose in life and some find the human condition too painful to bear. To remain positive about life can require a conscious effort that not everyone is able to make.

It is perhaps the mark of the truly ill person if these problems don't touch them at all. An individual may be so deep in their depression as to be unaware of what is happening in the world. Conversely, others can be so upbeat and 'positive' that they remain emotionally untouched by external events. The majority of people, including those with varying types of depression, fall in the middle of these extremes.

The reasons for depression are most probably interacting biological, psychological and social factors. I say probably because it is not yet known for certain what actually causes depression. Standard explanations focus on brain chemistry and psychological malaise but so far no one claims to fully understand this illness. Meanwhile scientists and doctors all over the world are devoting enormous amounts of time and money to increasing their understanding of the underlying biological nature of depression.

> While advances are happening all the time in the understanding of the human brain we really don't have a clue about the mechanism of depression – we only know about its terrible and destructive ability to ruin lives and diminish our potential for joy. Joy is not a word one hears very often today. How long is it since you asked a person how they are and they replied 'full of joy'? I would say that at least 40 per cent of my patients have some form of depression but few want to discuss it. They simply don't seem to understand that the success rate for people who have treatment and get their life back after depression is high. I would also add that I think significant emotional problems lie behind chronic illness in half of my patients.
>
> Psychiatrist, Sydney

While not knowing exactly what causes depression, recent research findings suggest that it is probably a neuro-degenerative disorder. It has been established that the continued stress of long-term untreated depression can cause physical changes to the brain. Ominously this research has also revealed that these degenerative changes to the brain can make sufferers more vulnerable to dementia as they age.

Depression often runs in families and some people are genetically predisposed towards it. Just as one person may have a tendency towards allergy or, say, bronchial problems, another will have a tendency towards depression. Then again, an individual can suffer depression and have no other relatives with the illness. People with depression should never be made to feel that somehow they are to blame for their illness.

Evidence that depression can have a genetic link is increasing and one recent study has shown a direct genetic link between emotionally distressing events and the onset of clinical depression. The isolated gene is a serotonin transporter called 5-HTT and people with a short form of this gene are more susceptible to depression. Intensive research in this area is continuing and some researchers believe that other genes will be discovered and that in the future it will be possible to screen people for a genetic susceptibility to depression.

There is a very small minority of psychiatrists and other health professionals who hold the view that depression is not a disease in itself. The arguments over the origins of depression are as passionate and intense as the continuing nature versus nurture debate.

> There are entrenched views held by doctors about depression like there are about other illnesses. The current orthodoxies about depression are coming under more scrutiny as we learn more and more about this illness. Unlike some practitioners, I have never subscribed to the belief that depression is purely biological. I don't think you can say with certainty that something is entirely psychological or biological. Depression is

extremely complex and cannot be slotted into one side or the other.

Senior psychiatrist, Sydney

Another doctor who sees many people with depression holds yet another opinion on the origins of this illness:

> My view is that depression is a disease of the central nervous system. The central nervous system controls everything that happens in our bodies and hence the diversity of symptoms. Most people can accept this. The difficulty is getting people to take the next step and accept that disease in our central nervous system alters the way we think. I dislike the term 'mental' versus 'physical' illness. When depression is no longer considered a mental illness but simply a disease, society and individuals will be able to accept and deal with it more effectively.

Physical illnesses, particularly chronic and terminal ones, can understandably cause a person to become depressed. Recent research, for example, suggests that major depression is more common in asthma sufferers than those without the respiratory disease. The survey indicated that one in seven asthma patients might have depression that is severe enough to require treatment, and for those who suffer severe asthma the rate is one in three. Findings presented at the 2004 Australian Asthma Conference suggest that depression affects the way asthma patients manage their condition by impacting on their sleep patterns, their ability to take medication correctly, keep medical appointments and follow an asthma management plan.

> I had about six months last year when my asthma was not well controlled. I have to take some responsibility as I was not following my usual medication program carefully and was working too hard. I was sleeping very badly due to

wheezing at night. I felt absolutely awful in myself, even when the asthma was not too bad. I was shocked when my doctor told me he thought I was depressed. In hindsight I realise I was. I was also alarmed that I had allowed the depression to creep up on me without taking some action myself. I feel I was very lucky to have a doctor who was prepared to broach the subject without any prompting. The depression has gone since I got my asthma under control.

Jack, aged thirty-seven

CHAPTER TWO

WHAT IS DEPRESSION?

Every human being, regardless of age, background, creed or culture, will experience mood swings. Sometimes we can feel sad for no particular reason. There are adaptive states of sadness that nearly everyone will experience at some time. We should not try to deny these feelings nor should we always feel the need to analyse them. Low feelings only become a problem if they persist over a long period of time and seem to 'take over' life.

Mild, short-lasting mood swings are a completely healthy part of the human condition. It is also healthy to be deeply unhappy and miserable when reacting to a major loss or crisis. These feelings of sadness, ranging from feeling a bit flat to extreme grief, are not to be confused with severe depression. It is when a mood outlives its context that it can become a serious threat to emotional health and functioning. Depression is an illness that is outside the control of the afflicted person.

> Grief is a completely normal response to life events such as the death of a loved one or a major disaster. People understand what grief is all about and it is accepted as a painful and stressful but healthy reaction to the event. Prolonged grief can trigger depression but most people experience an abatement of grief after a period of time. Prolonged and extended feelings of extreme sadness and melancholy are different to a normal grief reaction and if left untreated can lead to clinical depression.
>
> Psychologist, Sydney

What is Depression?

In western society particularly, people believe they have the right to feel happy and upbeat most of the time, and for many people sadness is seen as an affliction that should be avoided at all costs. These people may go to extreme lengths to avoid admitting that they are not feeling great emotionally. They may see it as a lack of personal control and a negative reflection on the way they are living their life. Like grief, however, sadness is often an appropriate response to a life event and may well trigger positive outcomes such as developing better self-awareness or clarity regarding a particular problem. Sad feelings, as opposed to depression, can be a way of gauging where we are in our life and how we are dealing with the world around us.

> Depression is a true monster. It can take over your life and you completely lose sight of the person you were before you became ill. It has to be the worst thing that has ever happened to me. I lost three years of life to this foul illness and it is still very scary and threatening for me to look back on those terrible times. I am forever indebted to my wonderful GP for recognising my problem and helping me struggle through periods of hell to where I am now. I did not respond immediately to treatment and I had to really work on the management of my illness – but it was worth it. I want to say that people should never give up or lose hope. Maybe I will be managing my illness for the rest of my life, but who cares? At least I have a life to live. The fact that I may have to be on a low dose of medication for life is a small cost to pay for the joy of not thinking about killing myself on a daily basis.
>
> Helen, recovering from depression

It is very hard for some people suffering from depression to acknowledge that they are ill and in need of medical or psychological help. The very fact that they are in a depressive state makes logical and informed decision-making more difficult, and it is very common for sufferers to let their symptoms reach crisis point before they seek help or even acknowledge that they need it. Conversely others are very in tune with their emotional state and will take action as soon as they realise they are heading for a depressive episode. The manner in which an individual deals with their depression has a marked impact on how quickly they recover.

There are people who are reluctant to admit that someone they care about is suffering from depression because they see it as something to be ashamed of, or they fear that they will somehow be blamed. This does not mean that they do not care or are fundamentally unkind. Awkward or defensive responses towards someone with depression can arise because people simply do not know how to cope. Unfortunately there are still large numbers of people in our society who find mental illness in another person very hard to deal with, saving their compassion and support for the physically afflicted person.

Some people I interviewed told of how hard it was to accept that a family member had depression. One parent said he still feels guilty about how he reacted to his son's depression, basically telling the boy to 'pull himself together' and get on with life. 'I told him he was a wimp, I can't believe how insensitive I was.' Many realised in retrospect how ignorant they had been about the illness and how little they understood mental health problems generally. Young people told of how scared they became when a parent had depression. 'You don't realise how much you rely on your parents being there for you until suddenly they are not there for you. When my mother got depression the whole family fell apart,' said one teenager.

Some depression sufferers I spoke with were angered and upset at the initial responses of their friends, family and work colleagues when depression was mentioned. Others reported losing their jobs and relationships and incurring suspicion and even hostility from family and friends after being diagnosed. Others spoke of the strain of having to hide their illness from employers and even some family members because they feared a negative or judgemental reaction.

What I needed most was an honest response from everyone around me. I was depressed, really depressed, and I knew it, but my therapist and family would simply not allow me to openly acknowledge my illness. I was stressed, exhausted, run down, coming to terms with a few life disasters, but I was not allowed to be depressed. I used the dreaded D word and they all refuted what was probably the loudest cry for help I have ever uttered. Even in the fog of depression I realised that they had a problem that was nearly as destructive as my illness. My parents and brother were simply too embarrassed to admit that they had a family member who was depressed. And I will never forgive my wimpy therapist for going along with them. I've survived and come out the other end due to the help and support of a great GP and some wonderful girl-friends who simply took me to this doctor and made me ditch the therapist. My family still finds it difficult to accept that I had true depression because, as my father said, 'No one in our family has been depressed. No one has let the side down.' Imagine thinking like that in the twenty-first century! He is not malicious, just bloody ignorant.

Megan Hasser, aged thirty

Some people with depression find that negative thinking colours every aspect of their lives. They have a bleak view of themselves, their future (if they believe they have a future) and the world at large. They believe that everything about their lives is terrible, that they are awful people and that each day is just another stretch of time to try to endure. Others can keep up a front and function fairly well while feeling absolutely wretched and despairing inside. It is amazing that some people with quite severe depression manage to hold down jobs and seem healthy to outside observers.

The strain of functioning in a normal and efficient manner was true hell. It was an Oscar-winning act. In a way I was relieved when my boss found me slumped in my car one lunchtime and asked me what was wrong. I let it all pour out. He was totally supportive and finally I could come clean, admit I had a problem and get help. It was only much later that this wonderful boss told me he had suspected something was wrong because he noticed my concentration had lapsed on numerous occasions.

Jenni Harper, aged forty

People without depression can accept that life is not perfect and that we all have parts of ourselves that we would ideally like to change. They don't allow the negative aspects of life to dominate their thinking.

It is not uncommon for some people to be relieved when told that their depression is induced by an imbalance of particular chemicals in their brain. They may even find this quite comforting, as it absolves them from taking responsibility for their feelings and the attendant problems caused by their illness. However, most doctors and therapists are adamant in the view that while a person with depression cannot help how they feel, they must try to take responsibility for their treatment or at least be involved in the decision-making.

Diagnosing depression

Depression cannot be diagnosed biologically. There is no blood test or any other test capable of identifying depression in a person. Doctors must rely on their own observations as well as what a patient says about themselves. This can make an attempt at diagnosis very difficult, as some people are reluctant to discuss their moods and emotional life or do not have the language skills to articulate their concerns and needs in a direct manner.

The word 'depression' is often used incorrectly. People say they are depressed when what they mean is that they are upset, angry, frustrated or just experiencing a normal lowering of mood. Standing at a city intersection on the way home from visiting my husband who is hospitalised with severe depression I overheard a brief conversation.'God I'm depressed. I booked the car in for a service and found out the engine needs major work.' It took a great degree of self-control to stop myself saying, 'Look sonny, if you think you're depressed, you should see where I've just come from.'

Wife of a depression sufferer

There is a big difference between sadness, a blue mood, despair and depression – an accurate diagnosis of what is really going on allows the right decisions to be made regarding the most appropriate treatment. Unfortunately only about 20 per cent of cases of clinical depression are initially correctly diagnosed, one reason being that depression can masquerade as a variety of physical ailments such as fatigue, changes in appetite or insomnia. When a patient complains to their GP about a physical ailment it is generally treated as such, and the underlying depression may remain undetected.

Depression can also cause impairment to physical health. Stress and anxiety (and for most people, depression is extremely stressful) have the ability to weaken the normal functioning of the immune system, and when the immune system breaks down physical illness can often result. Stress is clearly implicated in the development of some physical illnesses, including cancer and heart disease. In recent times medical researchers have noted that heart patients with depression have at least three times the risk of dying within a year of a heart attack if their depression is left untreated.

At times of stress, the human body produces hormones in the adrenal glands that are necessary for the body to cope with the demands of daily life. It is when these hormones are present in large amounts over a period of time that they stop being beneficial and start to have a negative impact. Too many of these hormones can slow healing, impair the immune system, increase blood pressure and affect blood glucose levels and bone density.

The term 'comorbidity' is used when there are two or more illnesses presenting at the same time. Depression is linked not only to physical illness but also to other mental illnesses and psychological disturbances including anxiety, schizophrenia, eating disorders, substance abuse, panic attacks and obsessive-compulsive behaviour. Differentiating between these conditions and determining the correct treatment program can be very difficult for doctors and therapists.

Because the experience of depression varies so greatly, people often reject a diagnosis of depression. In cases of major depression when a person doesn't understand the illness they can feel that their experience is being trivialised. 'You don't understand. I'm not simply depressed, I feel like I am going crazy!'

When I was diagnosed I was outraged. 'I am not depressed,' I told my doctor, 'I am just very stressed.' In a way I self-imposed stigma because I was so horrified at the thought of having an emotional imbalance. I was very, very defensive and angry. I now realise in hindsight that I was very ill indeed.

Depression undermines absolutely everything about who you are. Your ability to reason and think logically is stripped away. There is no escape from knowing that something is very wrong. I was unable to sleep and had constant fatigue. The fatigue made everything worse. Even when I managed to sleep I woke up feeling tired. I was able to hide the problem at work for quite a long time and then one day I could not go on. I was in my office and realised I was unable to go into a meeting that I was supposed to chair. I completely freaked out. I was fortunate in that I was able to take time off work without any problems and that I had the support of my colleagues. My wife and adult children were also totally supportive.

It was only when I was unable to function at my office that I finally went to a doctor. I still don't know what caused that single but serious depressive episode. I dwell on this at times but I try not to let it worry me. All I know is that I don't know how I would have got through my depression if I had not had such support. I feel very sorry for people who have to battle it alone.

Andrew St Clair, aged fifty-nine

The line between normal mood fluctuation and clinical depression is crossed when the feelings associated with a low mood increase in intensity, when they last for a longer period than normal and when a person's ability to function is impaired. These mood disturbances are frequently accompanied by a range of other symptoms, all of which can cause significant distress and impairment in social, occupational and other important areas of human functioning.

Lower than normal moods and other accompanying symptoms will generally have been present in most people for at least two weeks before clinical depression is diagnosed. It may be a transient mood fluctuation if it is present for less than this time and the person could well return to their usual state of mind without the need for any form of intervention.

One common characteristic of people with depression is a lack of self-esteem. Those with depression find that maintaining a sense of self-worth is just about impossible. Feelings of guilt, shame and self-loathing are also common. See the box on page 20 for other symptoms.

Before a diagnosis of depression is confirmed it should be established that the symptoms are not being caused by another illness or are not a reaction to a major life crisis. Even people suffering profound grief do not necessarily develop depression, although some of the symptoms can be the same. Other factors such as drug and alcohol consumption and individual personality traits can affect such things as mood changes, anxiety levels and sleep patterns. If you are experiencing some of the symptoms it does not necessarily mean that you have depression but you should consult your doctor and explain how you are feeling.

Common symptoms of depression

- reduced interest and enjoyment in activities and events and inability to experience pleasure
- insomnia or disturbed sleep patterns, or hypersomnia (sleeping too much)
- persistent pessimistic and negative thoughts
- marked changes in mood, such as increased levels of irritability, anger or anxiety
- lack of motivation
- lack of energy and increased feelings of fatigue
- impaired concentration and memory
- reduced sex drive
- changes in appetite and weight fluctuations
- recurrent thoughts of death or suicide

Types of depression

Most health professionals now accept that depression is not a single, distinct medical condition. There are a number of depressive disorder subtypes that can vary in severity and duration. Until recently, depression was seen as a disorder that was differentiated only in its degree of severity. However, there is considerable debate amongst the medical and scientific community as to how clinical depression and its various forms are best classified. Even within the broad classifications of 'major depression' and 'minor depression' there is a bewildering array of categories and subtypes. A further complication is that many symptoms are similar or overlap and merge, and some people suffer from more than one type of depressive disorder concurrently.

It is not necessary for the purpose of this book to detail the debate on the differences between the various subtypes. I have concentrated on the most widely used and understood classifications of depression and some of their most common subtypes. For those wanting more information on depressive subtypes, a good book is *Dealing with Depression – A Commonsense Guide to Mood Disorders* by Professor Gordon Parker.

The long-held belief that depression is either 'reactive' (a result of external factors) or 'endogenous' (caused by internal/genetic factors) is losing support. It is now more widely accepted that a person's environment and genetic history both play a part.

Sometimes a person suffering from bereavement or recovering from a major crisis can plummet from normal grief or anxiety into depression. Those who develop depression following an initial normal response to difficult or emotionally upsetting circumstances are described as suffering from an adjustment disorder with a depressed mood.

The term 'depression' is used to describe an illness that spans a huge spectrum. It is like the term 'cancer'. We would never give an account of an individual's experience with cancer without stating what type of cancer the person had. If I had a cancer removed from the lip and twenty years on I had no further experience with cancer, my experience would be very different from that of a person with cancer of the bowel who died within six months of being diagnosed. Again, a person who has lymphoma and undergoes a variety of medical and psychological treatments has yet another experience of cancer.

What of the person with chronic dysthymia who does not experience the torment of major depression yet never experiences life without the cloud of depression affecting their perceptions? These people may never seek treatment because they are never diagnosed or because they believe they can't have depression because it is not 'bad' enough or they can't relate to the stories of those with major depression? This is yet another experience of 'depression'. They suffer, not so severely, not so dramatically, yet their life is not as good as it could be and their suffering is very real.

Broken marriages, less than ideal parenting, loss of friendships, increased isolation, lack of realisation of personal
potential – who would place a judgement on suffering? The
experience of pain, loss and suffering is individual and I shy
away from placing any judgement on, or making comparisons
between, any people with depression. They all walk their path,
too often alone and too often misunderstood. I believe the current broad use of the term 'depression' without clarification
negates the individual nature of the experience and contributes to much misunderstanding and additional suffering.

Leanne Pethick, long-term depression sufferer
and founder of DepressioNet

Minor depressive disorders

Minor depressive disorders share a number of characteristics with
major depressive disorders and while the symptoms are usually
less numerous and less severe they still have the ability to cause
disruption and distress. Some people can experience long periods
of normal moods between episodes of feeling depressed, others
can experience symptoms on a regular basis and others still may
have only a single episode during a lifetime. It is also possible for a
person with a minor depressive disorder to experience major
depression.

Even those suffering from mild depression can still feel very bad
about themselves and often struggle with extreme feelings of guilt
and self-blame. There may often be, too, a concurrent anxiety disorder. Personality characteristics can influence how a person copes
with negative feelings and whether a low mood is going to slip
into a depressive state. Negative thoughts and feelings that are out
of proportion to the reality of an individual's life can persist for
weeks, months and even years.

Dysthymia

One of the most prevalent and probably one of the most under-
treated types of minor depressive disorders is dysthymia.

Dysthymia is a chronic form of depression and can sometimes start in childhood. With major depression, episodes can come to an end and there are periods of remission, however brief, when the person affected at least knows or remembers what it is like to feel relatively 'normal' and symptom free. Those with dysthymia suffer a 'smouldering', ongoing form of low-grade depression that can last for years and seldom remits spontaneously. It can be a life-long, corrosive experience and can have a dramatic effect on personality development.

> Dysthymia can be a constant, unremitting state, so that the person literally doesn't know what it feels like to be spontaneously happy or excited, or free of constant, gnawing worry. This is a truly horrible way to live. Common reactions to it are:
> - drinking excessively to escape the depression for a few hours
> - working excessively to 'use up' the free-floating anxiety and give a brief precious 'hit' of achievement
> - developing the coping device of a 'false self' – an outward personality that tries hard to go through the motions of normal emotion and function (often obsessive or perfectionist), as much an attempt to convince oneself as other people.
>
> This false self is artificial and stressful and doesn't reflect what one feels, or rather, doesn't feel. I think this can explain those cases one hears of fairly regularly, of someone who seems perfectly well adjusted and gives no indication of mental distress or unhappiness, and then is found by their partner or a friend hanging from a rope in the garage. They try and try . . . but then can't take it any longer and give up the struggle.
>
> It is especially frustrating that dysthymia is the most under-diagnosed form of depression yet it is so amenable to treatment by psychotherapy supported in the short or longer term by medication. I think it hypocritical of the Federal

Government to claim they are doing something about depression while refusing to fund under Medicare provision by psychologists of what is one of the most effective, clinically proven treatments for it.

Paul, aged fifty, a recovered dysthymia sufferer

Seasonal affective disorder (SAD)

Some people develop a depressed mood in response to certain climatic conditions. It is quite common for people to report feeling low or having a dose of 'the blues' during the grey and rainy days of winter. While most are only temporarily affected, others are so badly affected that they are diagnosed with a form of depression called seasonal affective disorder (SAD). These people can experience all or some of the symptoms of major or minor depressive disorders, but their symptoms disappear when the weather improves. A minority of people react badly to climatic conditions that are not related to winter. Some people find strong, relentless winds very disturbing and others find they become emotionally unsettled after experiencing days of strong, glaring, unremitting sunlight.

All types of minor depressive disorder should be acknowledged and treated, even if they are not severe or frequent.

Major depressive disorders

As I have said earlier there is a big difference between a transitory depressed mood and a depressive disorder. A person with a major depressive disorder will have experienced symptoms that impact on their daily activities for more than two weeks before a doctor will confirm a diagnosis of major depression. Most people with a major depressive disorder will notice changes in their appetite, energy levels and sleep patterns. Some will sleep more, others less, some will have an increased appetite and others will lose all interest in food. Feelings of worthlessness and hopelessness will emerge and may lead to suicidal thoughts. In some cases the person will attempt to take their own life. Varying degrees of social impairment will occur depending on the severity of the depression and on the personality traits of the individual.

Losing touch with reality, becoming delusional, hearing voices and developing hypochondria are further symptoms that can appear in a minority of sufferers. Some people may believe that they have a severe physical illness even when they have no worrying physical symptoms. Others imagine that people are out to get them and that the world in general is against them. When people suffer these symptoms they are sometimes described as having psychotic melancholic depression. It is essential that they receive immediate treatment because when they reach this stage they are very ill indeed.

Major depressive disorders can strike suddenly, can sometimes appear without an obvious cause and can affect people of all ages. They can vary widely in their severity and duration.

What happened to me is still unbelievable – for me, that is, not my doctor or my family. I had never had a day's depression in my life. I would describe myself as a happy person who coped well and positively with life's usual ups and downs. I had never had to survive a real tragedy. I used to think that the death of a child would be impossible to survive but all my children were well and happy when depression struck me like the proverbial bolt from the blue.

My husband had gone to work and I had stayed in bed to read the paper. Suddenly I felt a sense of the most awful anxiety and fear; perhaps terror would not be overstating the case. I thought I must have been having a panic attack. It was a terrible feeling and then I felt the most deep and painful emotions of true misery. I called my husband and I must have sounded so awful that he rushed home immediately. What ensued was awful, and after some days I was not better. I could not stop crying and I felt as if my life had finished. Yet nothing had changed. It did not creep up on me – it just attacked me. This weird condition was the beginning of a depressive episode that lasted for just over a year. I had transformed from a totally healthy and happy woman to a miserable, frightened and highly anxious person who could barely function. I became totally negative and thought that my whole life had been a failure. I apologised to my husband for being a terrible wife and to the children for being a bad mother. They were all appalled and reassured me I was a great person. Nothing made any difference to my feelings of worthlessness. I felt completely irrelevant in every way.

I went to a psychiatrist and was put on Zoloft and some other medication to help with the anxiety. I was also advised to have therapy, which I have to say did nothing for me because there was absolutely nothing in my life that I could think of that caused this emotional change. In fact I could not stand the therapist who asked me if I was harbouring secret worries that my husband might be having an affair. I thought that was extremely unprofessional, but my doctor said he thought it was a reasonable question. Fifteen months after my 'attack', as we call it in the family, I am completely well and am off medication. I have no sense of those awful feelings even lurking in my mind. It was a very frightening and very disturbing event. I now know how awful depression is.

I find it very odd that I suddenly just 'got depressed'. Sometimes I would prefer to think that I had a year of 'madness' rather than depression. Somehow it would be easier to accept.

Melissa Williams, aged forty-eight

Depression has caused our family the most unbelievable pain. It has caused me to vacillate between intense anger and intense despair. Once we were a normal family with the normal family problems – basically a united and happy little group. Today we are destroyed. We are traumatised by the erratic and aggressive behaviour of our eighteen-year-old daughter. It is a terrible and tragic story and I lay the blame on marijuana. Never let anyone tell you it is a harmless drug.

Our daughter became completely emotionally hooked on this so-called harmless drug and over a period of about a year underwent a total personality change. She is severely depressed and so far nothing seems to help her. She has seen doctors but often misses appointments and I am not sure if she is on medication at the moment, though I know she was prescribed antidepressants. She has lied, stolen, dropped out of university and is very abusive. Every member of our family is affected.

She is the eldest and the three younger children are terrified of her. However, we cannot find it in our hearts to ask her not to come home. If she did not have her old home as a place to come when she needs to feel safe I think she could lose it completely.

She turns up every few weeks or so and usually crashes out for a few days. She is either very quiet and passive, or very angry and abusive. I live in a perpetual state of misery and worry. I look at her baby photographs and photos of her school graduation and I just weep. Our clever, loving and kind daughter has disappeared. We were completely unprepared for this trauma and our lives have been completely turned upside down. We don't know what to do next.

Annie, aged forty-three

Bipolar mood disorder

Bipolar disorder affects up to 2 per cent of the population (both men and woman) and was known until recently as manic depression. It is a recurring condition that requires ongoing close monitoring and management. People who are diagnosed in adolescence may expect to have ten or more acute episodes during their lifetime.

With bipolar disorder the person suffers mood swings that alternate from depression to mania. During a manic phase the person can feel extreme emotions and display exaggerated and uncharacteristic behaviour. Their moods can be volatile and upbeat. These manic episodes are described as 'highs' because the person can feel absolutely fabulous. While some people's 'highs' can be quite mild, others are severe and lead them to engage in potentially self-destructive behaviour. Their elation can take them over the top, where they feel extremely energetic and lose all their inhibitions. They may experience increased sexual desire and engage in sexual activity that can be hurtful to those who love them. Some people go on wild spending sprees and run up large debts.

When a manic period escalates, the person can become delusional. They can lose touch with reality and slip into a psychotic state. People in the grip of psychosis can feel untouchable and omnipotent and some believe they are God or that God has asked them to do certain things. They can go without sleep for days as they revel in their newly acquired enlightened state. Some will write feverishly all day and night, often forgetting to eat. Others make incessant phone calls to their friends at any hour and their conversations and moods can range from extra loving to highly abusive.

Each manic episode is generally followed by a depressive period where the person can experience great remorse at how they behaved when 'high'. The term 'bipolar' can also be used to describe or diagnose people who only experience 'highs', where their mood is elevated well beyond their normal state. About 5 per cent of those suffering from bipolar depression experience only the highs.

> You feel you are getting a privileged insight into reality – an accelerated clarity – a new way of seeing the world. Everything is stripped of artifice. You are the one who can really understand what is happening. Other people seem to behave like sodden, dull lumps – you are the one who has the insight into what life is all about. I was disgusted at how dumb and

unenlightened my family seemed, particularly my poor mother who I really gave hell. Her constant love and support irritated me beyond belief because I thought I was the superior person and she seemed like a grovelling loser. It was absolutely horrible for the family when I was on one of my 'high' rampages.

Andrew, aged thirty-four

Alternating between one mood state and the other is called 'cycling'. The characteristics of cycling vary from person to person. Sometimes the cycles last for long periods without change, others alternate between mania and depression with regularity. Regular mood changes are called 'rapid cycling'. Some people can have long periods between cycles when they have neither depression nor mania. During this time a person can feel completely well.

It is a particularly distressing time for family and friends when a person is experiencing a severe 'high' because the sufferer is completely out of control and their behaviour can result in destructive and embarrassing outcomes for themselves and others.

When you come out of the mania you have to face the damage that you have done. Even during the mania I have flashes of the havoc I am causing, but when I'm manic I just don't care.

Susan, aged twenty-seven

Postnatal depression
Women are more likely to develop depression and anxiety following childbirth than at any other time in their lives, and postnatal depression appears to transcend all cultural, social and economic barriers. Generally there are three types of depression that can occur after giving birth, ranging from the 'baby blues' to postnatal depression and the very serious depressive state of puerperal psychosis.

Postnatal depression is not a single, distinct condition and is thought to be caused by a combination of physical, psychological and environmental factors. It can be triggered by an adjustment reaction to probably the biggest lifestyle change a woman and her partner have to make. Some couples find this adjustment more manageable than others.

The vast majority of women experience mood changes in the days following giving birth. The so-called 'baby blues' are very common and most new mothers have times when they feel weepy, emotional, lethargic and even anxious. This seems to be a normal experience, regardless of the initial excitement and joy after the birth. Fortunately the baby blues do not last long and usually disappear after a few days or even hours. Even those who have a relatively bad dose of the baby blues find that their mood will probably have settled after the first week or two.

However, there are some mothers who cannot shake off the blues and go on to develop a postnatal depressive disorder. There is often stigma attached to women who are not over the moon with joy following the birth of their child and who feel they can't cope or, even more distressing, do not instantly bond with and love their baby. Such situations can make women feel that they are unnatural mothers and compound the anxiety and depression.

In Australia postnatal depression affects around one in five women to varying degrees. After giving birth a woman's body is a maelstrom of hormonal activity. No one is sure of the precise role of hormones in inducing depression at what ideally should be a happy time, but hormones and other psychological factors do have a role in this type of depression.

Obviously an individual's circumstances can impact on the emotional state of the mother. Being a single mother without adequate support, being in an abusive relationship, having financial stresses, health problems and a predisposition to depression before or during pregnancy can contribute to a depressive state, but even women in good relationships who are surrounded by love and support can experience postnatal depression. A difficult and complicated pregnancy, labour or delivery can also be contrib-uting factors, as can a history of infertility or miscarriage.

The arrival of a new baby will always require some family adjustments – even when it is not the first child, the disruption and fatigue associated with a young infant are not totally unex-pected. For first-time parents, however, bringing a new baby home can be a devastating shock.

Many women see motherhood as an idealised role and some feel they cannot live up to expectations. They lose confidence and their self-esteem takes a beating. Often it is women who have excelled in high-powered professions who feel particularly powerless. They are used to being in control, engaging in decision-making and having job satisfaction in their professional lives. Then suddenly they find themselves still in a dressing gown at noon with a fractious baby, unwashed dishes and not a moment to themselves. If a baby is particularly unsettled and requires constant attention, a mother may have little time for anything other than tending the baby and trying to grab some sleep when the opportunity arises.

Medication during pregnancy

The Adverse Drug Reactions Advisory Committee has warned that women taking antidepressant drugs such as Prozac, Aropax, Zoloft and Cipramil during pregnancy may expose their babies to with-drawal and toxic effects.

Of further concern is a September 2005 warning from the Therapeutic Goods Administration, Australia's drug watchdog, that the drug paroxetine – sold in Australia as Aropax – is linked to birth defects. Pregnant women taking this drug should immediately review their treatment with their doctor.

It is generally recommended that the lowest possible dosage of selective serotonin reuptake inhibitors (SSRIs) should be used during pregnancy and during breastfeeding. Pregnant women should check with their GP before taking medications of any description, including vitamin supplements and other health-shop products.

Postnatal depression usually occurs within the first six months after the birth. The characteristics associated with this type of depression have many of the symptoms of generalised depression – fatigue, sleeping problems, changes in appetite, mood swings, emotional outbursts and anxiety. Mothers can become overanxious and obsessive over the baby's wellbeing – fearful that they will harm the baby or that it may die as a result of their ignorance.

An even more serious type of postnatal depression is called puerperal psychosis. This type affects about one in 600 new mothers and usually appears in the first few weeks following birth. The mother can suffer from erratic mood swings, delusions, hallucinations and suicidal thoughts. This behaviour can be very distressing to witness and often hospitalisation is required. However, the outcome is usually positive, with most women responding well to treatment. It is vital to seek medical help as soon as possible after the onset of symptoms.

Fathers, too, can experience depressive symptoms after the birth of a new child. Many men feel left out and isolated from the intimacy they previously had with their partner, who is now preoccupied with the baby. There is nothing like a new baby to kill the sexual intimacy and social life of parents. All these difficulties are magnified if the mother is depressed or not coping well.

Early recognition and diagnosis of the condition is important so that the depression will not be allowed to progress and become detrimental to the parents, baby and the rest of the family. The first step is to acknowledge that there is a problem and agree to seek help. The next step is a consultation with a GP or a community nurse. The most appropriate treatment will be started after an assessment of the individual. It is a good idea to book a double consultation so that there is time to talk in detail about how you are feeling.

I was quite okay for the first few weeks after giving birth. Our baby was eating and sleeping well and I was feeling perfectly fit. I joined a mothers' group and it was during one of those

gatherings that I realised I was feeling 'different'. I was usually an outgoing and friendly person who enjoyed people,
but suddenly I found that I did not feel like joining in the
excited chatter, or comparing notes about our babies. I had a
feeling of detachment and it started to become a permanent
feeling. I felt removed from reality – as if I was sort of walking
on air, away from what was around me. I felt this awful heav-
iness in my body and mind. Everything became an effort.
I overheard one of the mothers telling another that I was a
snob because I would never engage in conversations. My
husband noticed that my behaviour had changed and so did
my mother. I did not actually feel depressed. I sort of felt
nothing. It was like watching myself go through the motions
of life without actually feeling anything. I lost my appetite
and lost a lot of weight. I stopped going to the mothers' group
because I did not want to go anywhere or see anyone.

It was a friend of my husband (a nurse) who was the first
to suggest I had some form of depression. I did not agree but
was too apathetic to really object. I went to my GP and he
was onto my condition like a flash. He explained what postnatal depression was and said he believed I was suffering
from it. My doctor wrote out a gentle exercise regime for me
and also organised for me to see a dietician. I was referred to
a therapist who was helpful and after a few months my old
personality started to reappear and I felt as if I had returned
to earth. I was not prescribed medication though my doctor
told me this would be suggested if I showed no signs of
improvement.

I do not think my depression was severe, but I was completely detached and strange – it really was as if I was on a
huge daily dose of Valium. Sometimes I did not even bother
to shower, which is most unlike me. My husband has since
told me that I did not smile for about three months, but I was
unaware of this. I must have been a total bore to live with
and I do hope the baby will have no long-term problems

from having a mother who was there but not there. Unlike some of the stories I have read about postnatal depression, I did not cry or lose control of my emotions. My emotions just kind of shrivelled up.

Charlotte Phillips, aged twenty-four

CHAPTER THREE

TREATMENTS FOR DEPRESSION

It is important that everyone with depression be assessed and treated on an individual basis. However, there is vigorous, ongoing debate among medical and allied health professionals about the preferred modes of treatment. Some doctors and scientists will argue that there is not enough empirical evidence to recommend any form of treatment as the optimal treatment.

An early example of differing opinions in the treatment of depression is illustrated in the case of Melbourne psychiatrist John Cade who pioneered the use of lithium to treat bipolar disorder (manic depression) around 1949. He was a brilliant doctor and scientist but had no time at all for psychoanalytical theories such as those of Sigmund Freud. He was convinced that depression had a biochemical cause and was best treated by medication, and was highly critical of the 'talk' approach.

However, the broad consensus is that a combination of antidepressants and some form of psychotherapy is the most effective for the largest number of people. Then there are people who will not require a combination of treatments, responding well to one or the other. It is up to the patient and their doctor or therapist to work together to establish the type of treatment that will work best.

Antidepressants change the chemical balance in the brain by targeting very specific areas. The various forms of psychotherapy also change brain activity but in a different way. There is also a number of complementary or alternative treatments that are used by many people with varying degrees of effectiveness.

Many of the people I interviewed had particularly strong views regarding these various treatments. A number were opposed to antidepressants as the first mode of treatment, arguing that while drugs did help to a degree they did nothing to solve the underlying problem.

> Drugs for depression have been designed to help alleviate symptoms and not address the cause and that's because in my view the doctors don't seem to have a clue about the real cause of this bloody illness. I'm on drugs and I'm a bit better, but what happens when I stop taking the frigging tablets?
>
> Phillip, aged forty-four

Others expressed eternal thanks that they were given antidepressants, enabling them to regain a life that was not hell on earth. Some people were very critical of their therapists, whom they believed had their own agendas, were not flexible in their approach and did not tailor treatment to the individual. Others say their therapist saved their lives. Whatever a person's preferred mode of treatment, working with a therapist who is understanding, unpatronising and who treats each patient as an individual is crucial.

> It can be very confusing when you are desperately seeking answers, have finally found the courage to seek help and then discover your GP and therapist have completely different views on how you should be treated. When you are depressed it is often impossible to make decisions, you are feeling so vulnerable and hopeless. I was in a truly horrible position when my GP insisted I go on antidepressants and my therapist insisted I did not. I believe this period of indecision and confusion delayed my recovery by about a year. I eventually went to a second doctor who was prepared to talk on my behalf with the therapist – it worked out eventually because this doctor was prepared to spend time with me and included me in the decision-making.

I was on medication for a relatively short time and am
now very well.

Alison, aged forty-four

The first step in the treatment of all depression is a thorough and
careful assessment of symptoms followed by a frank and informed
diagnosis. Communication and frankness between patients,
health professionals and the friends or family are vital for the best
outcome in treatment and recovery. Unfortunately this is often
easier said than done, particularly when the people involved are
often emotionally distressed and vulnerable. Positive outcomes
involve being willing, if necessary, to undergo a range of treatments and in many instances being prepared for initial
disappointments. There is no quick fix for depression.

Unfortunately, there are many people with depression who are
neither diagnosed nor treated. Sometimes they do not even know
that they have it. The depressive illness itself can make people feel
so apathetic that they feel there is nothing that they can do to help
themselves. Many describe this feeling as 'heavy and leaden',
where everything, including such activities as washing and dressing, seems like an insurmountable task.

A GP is usually the first person to visit when seeking help. The
GP's initial response is crucial and their ability to supply correct
information and support is paramount to a successful outcome
for the patient. Diagnosing the type of depression before deciding on what treatment to follow is a responsibility that most
doctors take very seriously. Some GPs will feel comfortable and
confident treating their patients, others will elect to refer patients
to a specialist counsellor, psychologist or psychiatrist.

Most depression sufferers will want to know as much as possible about their illness and be involved in the decision-making
regarding their treatment. Others will be so detached with misery that they will show little or no interest in what the doctor
is suggesting for them. When a person is deeply depressed it is
often helpful for a family member or a good and trusted friend to

Legal and financial issues

There may be occasions when legal advice pertaining to the rights of a person impaired by mental illness will need to be taken by family members. Financial problems as a result of depression can add to what is already a stressful situation. Many creditors, especially those providing essential services such as water and electricity, are understanding when presented with real hardship and allow extra time for settling bills. It is best to address these problems as they occur and not let them build up. This is the time to remember that there are organisations and support groups that can help, even dealing with such issues as arranging extra time for paying off debts or helping with a budget. They can also provide advice pertaining to disability pensions and payment for carers. SANE (see the Useful Contacts and Resources chapter) has a national help line that refers people to relevant support services, including help with legal issues.

accompany them to the doctor where they can provide emotional support and be fully informed as to what treatment the doctor thinks appropriate. It is important for the patient to give their permission for their medical details to be shared with whoever is accompanying them or making medical decisions on their behalf. Sharing such information without informed consent can put doctors, family members or friends in a compromising and tricky situation if the patient is not in a fit state to fully understand their rights.

There are a number of different treatments for depression, including psychologically based therapies such as cognitive behavioural therapy (CBT) and interpersonal therapy (IPT). Pharmacotherapy treatments include a range of antidepressants and antipsychotic drugs. There is a widely held belief in the community that our health system is biased towards drugs as the first line of treatment for depression and that some GPs are poorly trained in their understanding of the specific psychological treatments available. Unfortunately there are occasions when a GP might prefer to send a patient to a psychologist or counsellor but they know that in many instances their patients cannot afford these types of treatment.

> When treating someone with depression I think it is very important to stress that recovery is achievable, that there is a good chance they will be cured. I try and instil a sense of hope in my patients. I try and help my patients get over that huge hurdle called 'hopelessness'. I strongly believe that the patient's attitude makes a big difference to the final outcome. It is not enough just to try and reduce symptoms – one should aim to eliminate them and then when the patient is better you can talk about the possible causes and future preventive strategies. I always tell my patients that remission is a realistic goal and I am convinced that my positive approach is important in giving even the most severely depressed person a sense that their illness can be beaten eventually.
>
> Psychiatrist, Adelaide

Depression is reportedly the most popular health topic looked up on the Internet and there are many creditable and informative websites (see the Useful Contacts and Resources chapter). Do beware of some sites, however, particularly from the United States, where information may be out of date, of poor quality and even misleading.

The following is an overview of the various treatments currently available. Once you know the options, you can have an informed discussion with your doctor as to what treatment will be best for you. Whether you are given medication, start therapy or undertake both concurrently will depend on the type and severity of your depression. If you have reservations or fears about any suggested treatments discuss them with your health practitioner and don't be fobbed off with unsatisfactory or vague answers.

Antidepressants

Antidepressant drugs have been used for the treatment of depression since the 1950s, and the different classes of antidepressants have increased dramatically. The latest type are called selective serotonin reuptake inhibitors (SSRIs) and have some advantages over the older class of antidepressant in that they can be tolerated more easily by more people. However, the older class of antidepressants such as tricyclics (TCAs) and monoamine oxidase inhibitors (MAOIs) are still prescribed and are very effective for some types of depression and some individuals.

The use of antidepressants is at an all-time high in Australia and the rest of the western world, yet there is fierce and passionate debate within the medical and scientific communities regarding the use and effectiveness of these drugs. Members of both the medical and lay communities are concerned that the increase in antidepressant use across Australia can be attributed partly to aggressive marketing by the pharmaceutical companies that spend millions on advertising.

> It is vitally important, in my view, that the first response to depressive symptoms is not to reach for the prescription pad. I strongly believe that the first course of action should be psychological therapy. It is important to try to understand what people are feeling and the reasons why they are feeling the way they do. Drugs don't work on the underlying problem, they don't help you understand the source of the pain. In my experience there are people on drugs for a depression they do not have. They are, instead, suffering from extreme emotions and the reasons for their distress need to be identified and dealt with.
>
> GP, Sydney

However, it is also widely acknowledged that antidepressants are an extremely effective form of treatment for many people. Antidepressants can restore normal function to many depression sufferers, they can help them rebuild their lives and have prevented others from attempting suicide.

> I was given 10 mg of Lexapro and felt much better, in fact, I felt amazing, in a very short time. I felt my IQ had tripled. When I have depression I am unable to think clearly. I now feel fabulous. I feel that at last I have a life back. I just wish that I had been prescribed this drug earlier. Talking to a therapist did absolutely nothing for me. I believe that my depression must have been chemically based because it has gone, but I still have the same life problems that were in my life when I was depressed, except now I can deal with them. Three cheers for antidepressants!
>
> Thomas, aged forty-seven

Still, it is important to recognise that antidepressants are not the appropriate treatment for everyone with depression and can make some people worse. The media has reported some horrific stories about antidepressants making people suicidal, aggressive and extremely violent. Some antidepressants are suspected of exacerbating self-harm tendencies in young recipients. Towards the end of 2004, the United States Government ordered that all antidepressant drugs be sold with a prominent warning to doctors that the medications can increase the risk of suicidal thoughts and behaviour among children and adolescents.

Following these disturbing reports, Australian doctors have been urged to exercise caution when prescribing antidepressants to young children and adolescents. There is also some evidence collated by the World Health Organization (WHO) that, contrary to what was originally thought, certain SSRIs can cause degrees of physical dependency in some people.

> My neurochemistry was altered dramatically by the antidepressant drug I was prescribed. I truly believe it was not

my depression that made me feel crazy and suicidal but the effect of the drugs. I am still on the same drug but the dose has been decreased. However, I have changed my doctor because the doctor that originally put me on antidepressants actually *increased* the dose when I told him I was worse. I had never felt suicidal before I went on medication. Now I am on a dose that agrees with me and I feel back in control of my life. I strongly advise people to contact their doctor if they feel they are having a bad reaction to medication and insist that the doctor listen to them. I was just fobbed off and things got a lot worse before they got better. Fortunately I was not so depressed that I was unable to make a decision to seek further help.

Samantha, aged thirty-five

Before prescribing antidepressants doctors should discuss the possible side effects and also make clear that once a drug is prescribed it can be several weeks before it has any discernible benefits. Doctors should also be informed of any other medication being taken, as some antidepressants interact badly with other drugs and some need to be accompanied by dietary restrictions. Combining antidepressants with alcohol and other substances can cause major problems.

Some people believe that taking antidepressants is a sign of personal weakness and view this form of treatment as a last resort. This is an erroneous and somewhat rigid view and one that would be strongly rejected by the large numbers of people who have benefited from antidepressant medication. Overcoming psychological resistance to medication can in fact be viewed as a brave and positive move.

I become very angry when I hear members of my own profession bad-mouthing antidepressants. I know and I am sure all doctors know that antidepressants have saved lives and will continue to save lives. If used correctly they can work miracles for some people. Drugs do not directly address the causes of depression, of course they don't, but they have enabled many patients to reach a level where they are able to address issues and deal with their illness much more effect-ively than they could without medication. I also get very angry when some patients intimate that I am probably in the pay of a drug company to push their product. One patient that I believed desperately needed medication for his depres-sion actually asked me if a drug company had sponsored my recent holiday in Bali. I was livid!

GP, Melbourne

It is vital to have a trusted doctor, one who is prepared to spend time getting the treatment right and who will also monitor the patient after treatment has been started. Different people will respond differently to different types of antidepressants. Trial and error is usually the only way that a person can find the drug and the dose that suits their particular needs. About 30 per cent of people will not respond to the first drug they are offered.

I have suffered from depression on and off since I was a teen-ager. My parents split up when I was about twelve, and while they told all their friends that they were having an amicable divorce and would always be friends, it was devastating for me. I hated having to spend time with each one separately at their respective houses and I desperately wanted them to be together. I always put my depressive times down to the emo-tional pain I went through at this time of my life.

I was put on antidepressants by a GP when I was about twenty and even though I asked for information about the medication, he told me to read the information enclosed with the medication and that that would be enough. The information did not explain that the medication could make some people rather uninhibited and change their personal-ity to some degree. I was one of those people. I had quite a

dramatic personality change in a very short time after start-
ing the medication.

To say I was uninhibited would be putting it mildly.
I became highly sexual and had affairs with a number of
men, leaving a lot of emotional pain and disruption in my
wake. I even changed the way I dressed. I felt great for a few
months but slowly this flirtatious, sexy, flighty and fake person disappeared and the real me came back. By nature I am
a rather shy person and certainly don't enjoy sleeping
around. My depression was definitely better but I felt terri-
bly remorseful and embarrassed by my wild behaviour.
I actually lost a couple of long-term girlfriends. It was pretty
devastating.

I decided to stay on the antidepressants for a while longer
because I realised that without them I could easily slip back
into a hole. I have since found out that this side-effect is not
uncommon, but I have found it extremely hard to get satisfaction in my quest for more knowledge. The doctors know
the different brands but seem to have very limited knowledge about exactly how the different types of antidepressants
work and their potential side-effects.

I understand that antidepressants change your brain
chemistry, but I don't ever again want to feel that drugs are
changing my personality. It was a very upsetting and horrible
experience.

Ruth, aged forty-one

Some recent research by Dr Chee Ng at the University of Melbourne showed that ethnicity may have a role in how people
respond to antidepressants. In a pilot study Dr Ng was able to
demonstrate that those of Chinese background are more sensitive to antidepressant medication, responding to lower doses,
than Caucasians. This suggests that genetic factors may deter-
mine how the body metabolises medication through the liver
and into the bloodstream, or how the medication affects the

functioning of the brain. While a lot more work needs to be conducted on the relationship between ethnicity and antidepressants, these new findings add to the understanding that antidepressants can produce dramatically different outcomes from person to person.

Psychological treatments

Psychological treatments involve verbal communication between the patient and qualified therapists. There are many styles of psychological treatments and they are often referred to in the profession as the 'talking therapies'. What the various therapies have in common is the aim to develop a trusting relationship (known in psycho-speak as 'a therapeutic alliance') between the trained professional and the patient. These treatments require a fair degree of commitment to understanding what your therapist is telling you and applying it to your life. While there is time and effort involved, the outcome can be very effective and rewarding for many people. Some people with depression are too ill and unmotivated to be suitable candidates for therapy and simple supportive counselling and antidepressants may be more effective during this period of their illness.

Some talking therapies are more effective for depression than others, and some appear to be as effective as drugs in the treatment of mild and even severe depression. Individual cognitive characteristics can influence a person's interpretation of negative life events. Trained professionals can teach people coping strategies to deal with the problems that may be causing their depression and to reverse negative thinking patterns.

Cognitive behavioural therapy (CBT), interpersonal therapy (IPT), supportive counselling, marital and family therapy and long-term psychoanalysis have all been shown to be effective in varying degrees for the treatment of depression. Recent research suggests that depression responds equally well to a surprising variety of psychological interventions so it is worthwhile becoming informed of your options and not automatically accepting the first line of therapy suggested. Sometimes trial and error is the only way to find the right therapy or combination of therapies for a person. Whatever type of therapy you choose, it is important to check that the sessions are being conducted by an accredited professional. You must have confidence in the clinical aptitude and professionalism of the therapist and most people find it counterproductive to stay with a therapist they don't like.

> We took our daughter to an eminent child psychotherapist when she became very unhappy after we had moved house. The sessions went on and on, week after week, and our daughter remained unchanged in mood. It was during a family discussion at home that we finally discovered that it was not only the house move that was upsetting her but also the change from a small rural school to a large state school. We moved her to a smaller school and it was like a light being turned on. She thrived in the more gentle and caring environment. The therapist who seemed reluctant to stop our visits warned that the unhappiness would continue or re-emerge as we had not resolved the underlying problems. She was wrong. Our daughter has never looked back and has enjoyed school ever since.
>
> One issue that really disturbed me was when the therapist freaked out during a family session because my daughter called me by my Christian name and not Dad. The therapist claimed that by asking my children not to call me 'Dad' it was a sort of denial of my parental role or responsibility. Not only was this tripe, but I knew from my readings about psychotherapy that it was downright unethical to make such a value judgement. Be selective and choosy about what type of therapy is right for you and be equally as careful about individual therapists. There are some terrific therapists and there are some shockers, in my opinion.
>
> Giovanni, aged fifty

Cognitive behavioural therapy

CBT aims to change negative thought patterns and beliefs. Unlike psychoanalysis it does not concentrate on the past but focuses on the present. Depression and other emotional disturbances can be the result of distorted perceptions of life and negative thinking. When you are depressed it is hard to recognise or accept that you have any positive qualities. Negative thinking becomes entrenched. Through a structured process of formalised techniques the therapist will teach the patient to recognise that there is a connection between mood, behaviour and thought. By identifying the errors in the thinking process the therapist is able to help the patient change their maladaptive behavioural and emotional patterns. When the thinking patterns are changed or modified, the depressed mood can be alleviated.

> I have for many years had severe anxiety and low self-esteem. I would often engage in very negative internal 'head talks'. My GP became quite insistent that I undergo some therapy and eventually I agreed. CBT challenged my habitual negative ways of thinking and made me much more realistic in my perceptions. I was even able to see the genuinely negative things in life in a truer light. I had intensive CBT for about three months and it has changed my head and life. I think my depression was triggered by my endless anxiety. It was a horrible way to live. One of the early philosophers said, 'It is not the things of this world that hurt us but what we think about them.'
>
> Stanley, aged thirty-two

Interpersonal therapy

IPT focuses on addressing current interpersonal problems that may have triggered the onset of depression. It is designed to improve relationships and social functioning. Rather than attempting to change aspects of personality it aims to help the depressed individual deal with existing issues in their life such as unresolved grief or anger, difficult relationships, disputes and social insecurities. The therapist will help people change their responses and beliefs in relation to these issues.

> As a chronic sufferer of depression I was originally a great believer in Freudian analysis. But after some time I came to the conclusion it was not for me. It was just too long and drawn out to help me with the way I was feeling now. I will not say it is not for everyone, but I certainly had better, more immediate help with interpersonal therapy.
>
> Lee, aged sixty-four

Transcranial magnetic stimulation

TMS involves the application of pulsed magnetic fields to the surface of the brain with the intent of stimulating or changing brain activity. The procedure involves a coil being placed on the scalp near the front region of the brain. The coil is connected to a machine that generates the electrical current. It is not yet clear how this helps depression symptoms. One theory is that the repeated stimulation alters the nerve cell activity in the front regions of the brain, resulting in mood change.

Individual treatments usually take between ten and twenty minutes and unlike electroconvulsive therapy (ECT) no anaesthetic is required. In fact many people return home or go to work immediately following their treatment.

After many years of continuing evaluation and research, the trials of this relatively new treatment are promising. There have been positive results for people who previously had treatment-resistant depression. Indications are that TMS will become accepted as a therapeutic treatment for depression in the future and will be available outside the strictly controlled and limited hospital environments where it is currently offered.

Electroconvulsive therapy

Few medical treatments are as misunderstood and cause as much concern as ECT but a high percentage of people who have had this treatment are prepared to receive it again.

ECT involves giving the patient a general anaesthetic and a muscle relaxant to minimise muscle contraction. Then a brief, measured dose of an electrical current is passed across the brain through electrodes attached to one or both sides of the scalp. The patient will experience a brief convulsion. The response of the nerve cells in the brain to the electrical current enables them to release chemicals that immediately impact on the patient's mood.

ECT is usually given about three times a week for a course of six to ten treatments depending on the individual response. Temporary side-effects can include haziness, memory loss and headaches. There are no known long-term side-effects.

Doctors take great care in deciding who will benefit from this treatment. ECT is used for people who are so severely depressed that they are unable to eat or drink, or who are not responsive to medication. It is also used for people at risk of suicide, and those with severe psychosis or mania.

The world's first ECT treatment was administered in 1938 and was given without a general anaesthetic. In the early days it was used rather indiscriminately and developed a rather terrifying reputation. Stories of the horrors suffered by patients intensified after the 1970s movie *One Flew Over the Cuckoo's Nest*. Many people seemed to think this movie had the authority of a documentary and believed that what they saw on the screen was how it really was. There have been moves in the past to ban or restrict its use. ECT still has a reputation of being 'scary' amongst people who are not fully informed about current methods of delivery, but it is a safe and effective treatment and has been life-saving for many people with depression and other mental illnesses.

I was undergoing a major internal disintegration. I was being devoured by a depression that invaded my mind and spirit. The horror and terror that I went through as I watched myself fall deeper and deeper into a black, bottomless pit is indescribable. Antidepressants made little or no difference. I have had some serious physical illnesses in my life but depression has been by far my worst 'bad health' experience. Death seemed preferable to life but I did not even have the energy to think about actually doing something about killing myself. When my doctor suggested ECT I was really too far gone to care. I agreed because my wife begged me to try it. She saw it as a last resort. The results for me were nothing short of a miracle. I have a life back and if my depression returned I'd be queuing up outside the clinic for more ECT.

Simon, aged sixty-five

Deep brain stimulation

This technique involves surgically implanting electrodes in a targeted area of the brain thought to be involved in depression. The procedure was developed after researchers observed that a particular region of the brain is metabolically overactive in people with treatment-resistant depression. When the electrodes were activated patients reported immediate improvement in their mood and reported feeling calmer and more alert.

This treatment is still very new and if and when it becomes available, is recommended for use only on those people who have suffered depression for many years and have found no relief from such treatments as medication, ECT and psychotherapy.

Professor Jeff Rosenfeld and Associate Professor Paul Fitzgerald of the Alfred Psychiatric Research Centre have recently commenced the first Australian study of this treatment for depression sufferers. Paul Fitzgerald stresses that the trials will involve only people with a history of 'highly resistant depression'.

Phototherapy

Commonly called light therapy, this form of treatment is used for people suffering from seasonal affective disorder (SAD), a winter-onset subtype of minor depressive disorders. This treatment consists of a measured dose of high-intensity artificial light shone into the eyes. The treatment is based on evidence that a lack of sunlight during winter can cause a shift in the body's circadian rhythms, which then affects mood. Some doctors believe that this form of treatment can, for a minority of SAD depression sufferers, be more effective than antidepressants.

Hospitalisation

One of the most difficult scenarios for a family is when a family member suffering from depression does not recognise that they need urgent treatment. It is often impossible to reason with a person when they have such a severe mood disorder that their mind is unable to engage with reality. There are times when there is simply no alternative than to admit a person to hospital. The need for hospitalisation is indicated when the family or carer believes there is a suicide risk or when symptoms suddenly become much worse.

There are times when a depressed person is so ill that they simply cannot be looked after at home. Hospitalisation can be voluntary or involuntary. An involuntary admission is even more upsetting for the family. The professional assistance and advice of a psychiatrist and sometimes the police will be required for involuntary admission. This is a time when carers and families need support and help, since they will be feeling distressed and even guilty at what they have had to do.

> The most confronting experience of my life was when my mother was taken to hospital as an involuntary patient. This will sound shocking but it was confronting for me because I

realised how pleased and relieved I was that she was going away for a while, meaning our family could have a break from her terrible moods. I was quite devastated at what a sense of relief I felt, especially as my father was a weeping wreck. Dad was feeling guilty at having called Mum's psychiatrist and the police after she became more out of control than usual, but my brother and I told him he had made the right decision.

Our family has lived for over three years with our mother's bipolar depression and to be frank there have been times when it has been sheer bloody hell. The hardest part is that when Mum is okay she is a terrific person to be with and we love her. But sometimes I hate her when she goes into a depressive mood. Her lows are in many ways worse than her highs. Until the last high episode, when she was actually violent with Dad, she was often quite funny and we could cope better. When she is low she is super-irritable and can say very nasty things. Mum was in hospital for three weeks and it was the most peaceful time we had had in ages. Even Dad admitted that it was a relief not to be anxious about what she was doing all the time. We had meals together like a normal family and it was great. Dad went to see Mum in hospital every day but the doctor told us kids to stay away while she was being treated. I reckon he knew we all needed a break.

Since Mum has been home she has been okay and now it is nearly three months since she went to hospital. We live in hope. One positive thing is that Mum is at last talking openly about her depression and has promised us she will really work on trying to stay well. This is a real breakthrough as she had refused to talk about her illness before. My brother actually asked a friend around for a meal last week. That is something none of us have wanted to do since Mum got sick.

Kevin O'Reilly, aged eighteen

Complementary and self-help therapies

According to recent surveys of community attitudes towards treatments for depression, large numbers of people have an inherent distrust of mainstream medicine and say that they prefer to consult family, friends and community support groups rather than general or mental health practitioners and have a preference for complementary and self-help therapies such as yoga, herbal remedies, exercise, massage, acupuncture, visualisation and bright-light therapy. Others opt for an integrated approach where they combine traditional and complementary therapies.

While not all complementary treatments have been fully evaluated, initial trials are promising for a number of them. St John's wort (*Hypericum perforatum*) is one of the most popular alternative remedies used for the treatment of mild to moderate depression. Recent trials have concluded that standardised extracts of the herb were equally effective as some antidepressants. The chemistry of this herb is complex and it should never be used in conjunction with other medication without medical advice.

A number of people swear that their depression has been helped by taking a dietary supplement of omega 3 in fish oil tablets, or by boosting their consumption of oily fish. Fish is a natural source of omega 3 fatty acids, and countries with a low level of fish consumption report higher levels of major depression. Controlled trials are currently underway to establish if there is evidence for these claims, but the anecdotal evidence does look promising.

There is evidence that other complementary and self-help treatments can be effective for depression sufferers. The amino acid SAMe, light therapy, air ionisation, massage, yoga, breathing and relaxation therapy have been found to benefit some sufferers in both the short and long term. Like prescription medication, individual responses to these treatments vary widely but they are certainly worth considering.

I found some simple yoga exercises and deep breathing very helpful while I was slowly reclaiming my life after depression. When I was feeling particularly bad, which was usually in the morning, I put on some gentle, hypnotic-style music and started my yoga movements followed by deep breathing. I have kept this up even since returning to work, where I don't lie on the floor (the boss might find this a bit much!) but go through a series of stretching movements in the tea-room. My work associates have been more interested than being critical of what I do and a number, who sit in front of computers all day, have started their own little exercise routines. During my depressed periods I find that I gain a feeling of greater calmness after half an hour of controlled relaxation. It was a good tool in my fight against my plummeting emotions during the worst times of my depression and now assists me in my maintenance phase.

Jenny Oldham, aged thirty-nine

When approached in a sensible and considered way, alternative treatments may well have benefits for depression and general health. However, it is concerning that many people receiving them may have never had proper medical diagnoses. The concern is that in some instances they may have severe depression and/or other mental or physical illnesses that could deteriorate without medical intervention and support. It is also important to remember that some supplements ('natural' medications) can interact badly with prescription drugs, alcohol and other substances.

It is particularly wise to approach the more controversial complementary treatments such as distance healing with a degree of caution. Treatments for depression, whether they are mainstream, alternative or self-help, should be discussed with a qualified health practitioner so that an educated choice can be made.

Laughter

Psychology professor Charles Schaefer from the Fairleigh Dickinson University in New Jersey believes that even a minute of laughter on a regular basis can help lift a low mood and improve psychological wellbeing – even when there is nothing to laugh about and the laughter is forced. Professor Schaefer uncovered the beneficial effect of artificial laughter and fake merriment during a number of experiments he conducted with his students. While the brain might know that the laughter is manufactured, the body does not. Once the brain signals the body to laugh, endorphins are released, which in turn alleviate stress and anxiety.

One depression sufferer, at the suggestion of his psychiatrist, bought all the Fawlty Towers videos, and in one sitting watched several hours of Basil's lamentable efforts to run his hotel.

> I was not able to hold back my laughter. It was the first time my wife had heard me laugh for a long time. Since then we've tried to watch a funny video at least twice a week, and I do think I feel better after a good belly laugh. The very act of sitting down with my wife and watching a comedy together is a move forward because I have not had the heart or energy to partake in any joint activity for a long time. It has been good for our relationship as we have actually relaxed together and my depression has not been the number-one topic of conversation.
>
> Joel Weiss, aged seventy-four

CHAPTER FOUR

RECOVERING FROM DEPRESSION

Once depression has been diagnosed and treatments start to kick in, it is time to look at what can be done to keep mentally and physically healthy and to help prevent the depression worsening or returning. While preventing the onset of depression is usually beyond a person's control, taking an active role in long-term recovery is positive and reaffirming. There are practical things to do, sometimes in conjunction with therapy or medication, that can help maintain mental and physical wellness and improve the quality of life.

Support from family and friends

For the person with depression, emerging from the emotional isolation and misery of their illness can be very challenging. The re-emergence of the old self, of who you were before depression struck, can be quite confronting and even scary. As one sufferer said, 'It is like being born again, only this time you are not innocent to the pain of depression and you know how this illness can destroy or distort who you are.'

It is important not to expect too much too soon, and to accept the fact that recovery can be slow, perhaps even imperceptible, on some days. This is a time when it is particularly important to have the support and encouragement of family and friends – recovery is a harder road for those who don't. A trusted friend, doctor, psychotherapist or psychiatrist can also play an important part in the healing and recovery process.

I believe in the mind–body connection and I truly believe that your attitude towards your illness has a big role in maximising the effectiveness of treatment and the eventual outcome. I think it is important to try and be positive about a future, to try to believe that everything will pass. I try not to hate myself and to keep an image of what I am like when I am not in the grip of this monster. Even when I am in the deepest depressive hole, there is a tiny part of me that hangs onto the thought that 'it can't, it won't always be this bad'. I think that hope is a major ingredient in the recovery process. I owe much to two close friends who never lectured me or judged me while I was so ill. They were just there for me and listened to my boring ravings about how awful I felt for hours on end. Their support helped me keep hope alive.

Alan, aged twenty-four

Living with a depressed person

In some instances a person with depression is actually the main carer and/or provider in a household. The burden of having depression, looking after a family and holding down a job can take its toll. People in this position can become irritable, highly stressed and develop physical illnesses, and naturally their behaviour and state of mind will impact on family members and work associates. If the sufferer is not receiving treatment for their depression, the situation will undoubtedly deteriorate and everyone's suffering will increase.

There is no denying that loving and living with a depressed person is difficult, and can be emotionally and physically draining. It is important that all those involved in supporting the person try to look after their own wellbeing and if possible not feel that they have to bear the sole responsibility. If the carers become exhausted, the family difficulties are only compounded. Family and friends of a depressed person have to recognise that they too have needs and must take steps to ensure that these needs are met. This is not always easy to achieve and there are times when a partner, parent, other family member or friend may themselves feel despair at the situation they are in.

Some members of the family can also feel very angry towards the person with depression who is causing all this havoc and pain in their lives. This is quite a normal response, but places a further strain on other family members who feel they must try to diffuse the anger.

No matter how much you love them or how close to them you are, there will be times of great uncertainty where you will not know how to act or respond to the moods and behaviour of the person with depression. Some carers are unaware of the various professional help and treatments available for depression and may struggle on for years without support or professional advice. Support groups can be helpful, as can phone help lines, because people then realise they are not the only one in the world trying to cope with these issues. Sometimes just talking to a professional counsellor about the situation can make a support person feel better.

I actually went to my husband's GP, and while he was unable to discuss my husband's medical details he was able to help me with advice for my own despair and point me towards a therapist and support group. My husband clearly was depressed and would not admit it or discuss his moods with me. Every time I tried to broach the subject he became hostile and withdrew into himself even further. By the time I sought support I was an emotional and physical wreck. I have been able to cope better since I have been having counselling and have had the opportunity to talk with others who are going through the same experience. Sharing the load has helped me.

Helen, aged sixty-two

Investing time in friendships can be very rewarding and just reaching out to someone who cares about you can have positive benefits.

When we are happily communicating with someone our body releases the hormone oxytocin, which can have a positive impact on depression and stress levels. Reducing isolation and loneliness by encouraging participation in some form of community activity can also be helpful.

Unfortunately many people with depression become antisocial and sever contact with friends during their illness. Others can be rude and abusive to well-meaning friends and this can make it embarrassing and awkward to re-establish contact once the depression starts lifting. However, good friends will usually be understanding and few people will lose true friends through their illness. It may help to explain to friends just how depression can change behaviour and character.

> Climbing out of the huge and all-consuming black hole of depression was the longest journey of my life. But as the days passed and my treatment started to kick in, the tiny gleam of hope that had prevented me from killing myself grew stronger and stronger. One day I realised that I had been awake for a few hours and had not thought about or been conscious of depression – and it had been my constant companion for over a year. This was when I phoned my husband at work and said, 'I'm winning, I'm winning.' We both burst into tears of joy. Two weeks later we gave our first dinner party for at least a year. I had conversations with friends I had retreated from, and the subject of my depression was not brought up. The old me was back and it was wonderful. I have rejoined the human race.
>
> Juliet, aged forty-seven

It should be stressed that all depressive states have the ability to impact on a person's life and the lives of the people around them. Depression in any of its various forms is not an illness that the person affected can afford to ignore, for even cases of mild depression can last for long periods if left untreated and can have devastating effects on the person. It is now recognised that untreated depression can lead to an increase in physical illness and can also impair the sufferer's capacity to make good decisions about eating and exercise habits. Very few people with severe depression are able to maintain a healthy lifestyle.

Nutrition

Good nutrition is an important requirement in maintaining good health and this can often be a problem for people with depression, as some sufferers lose their appetite and eat very poorly, and others binge on junk food and gain too much weight. Both problems require intervention and a GP is the first person to approach for advice on how to deal with eating disorders. The GP may advise therapy and a visit to a dietician if the problem is not easily resolved. There are strong links between depression and obesity and for many it is an ongoing and difficult battle.

Exercise

Physical inactivity, and its attendant health problems, is one of the major public health issues of the twenty-first century. Our sedentary lifestyle is contributing to the obesity epidemic, many other physical ailments and is also associated with stress, anxiety and depression. There seems to be enough evaluated evidence to suggest that regular exercise can be helpful for people with depression. Certainly, exercise stimulates the production of endorphins in the body, and when released into the system these endorphins produce an increased sense of wellbeing.

Not all depression sufferers agree that exercise is helpful, and a small minority report feeling worse, but the general consensus is that regular exercise helps bring about positive mood changes and certainly helps with physical fitness.

Exercise such as tennis, golf, walking in groups and dance or yoga classes can be particularly effective because of the social interaction with other people. People with depression often feel withdrawn and tend to shun social contact. Group exercise can provide non-demanding interaction with others and help rebuild social skills and confidence.

Recovering from a depressive episode does not happen overnight and it can be weeks before any real improvements are discernible. If possible, some form of exercise should be encouraged even when the depressed person is still feeling low. In the long-term, exercise can also alleviate some of the physical health risk factors for depression, such as obesity and heart disease. Exercise improves blood lipid levels and counters the tendency to obesity that can lead to heart disease. Try and exercise as much as possible but be sensible and match your exercise to accommodate your age and general level of fitness. Do not start an exercise program without having a check-up with your doctor, particularly if you are over thirty-five or have not exercised for some time.

Relaxation techniques

Relaxation (including meditation) is a widely used behavioural technique to help manage stress, anxiety and depression. There are many good books available on relaxation techniques, or your GP or therapist should be able to suggest one for you. Many relaxation and stress management techniques can be done at home without any financial outlay for special equipment or classes. Commitment and perseverance are the main requirements if beneficial results are to be achieved.

Conclusion

People with severe depression can make sincere efforts to eat well and exercise but very often their depression will sabotage their good intentions. For a person with depression, and for their family, there are many moments when life seems to be a continuous 'one step forward and two steps back'.

Our son is slowly coming back from the true hell of a long depressive episode but he just doesn't seem to be able to help himself get fit. He does go to his therapist and he does take his medication but he won't take his doctor's advice and exercise at all. Can you imagine how difficult it is for us to see this boy sit around all day munching on chips and chocolate bars? We know our son is trying, but so far the therapist cannot get through to him that he has to start taking responsibility for his overall health. He is twenty-four so we can hardly follow him to the shops and stop him buying junk food or take his dole money. Depression has left our once athletic and good-looking son a big slob. We can only hope that as his depression recedes he will want to be fit and attractive again.

Hannah, aged fifty-two

CHAPTER FIVE

PROFESSIONAL PERSPECTIVES

The following people are all involved, in various capacities, with the treatment of mental health problems. All of them have experience with treating depression and their comments and opinions are helpful not only for depression sufferers but for their family members, friends and workplace associates.

The biological psychiatrist

Dr David Grounds, MB, BS, FRACP, FRANZCP, is a biological psychiatrist who has a special interest in mood disorders. He is a consultant to the Melbourne Clinic, the largest private psychiatric centre in Australia, which he helped establish. He has been in private practice as a psychiatrist since 1971 and is an expert on antidepressants. He is also a strong believer in the benefits of exercise in the treatment of depression.

The word 'depression' is often used to describe unhappiness or a low feeling. It is too often used in an unsuitable context – clinically depressed is *not* the way a Collingwood supporter might feel on a Saturday night! True clinical depression is a physical illness manifesting in both emotional and physical symptoms.

I am not sure if there is more depression about today than there was in the past. We have better surveys and methods of measuring the amount of depression in the community and I think this probably accounts for what could be attributed to an increase. The fact that the general community is more aware and informed about depression is an improvement on the past when mental health was something that was swept under the carpet and not spoken about.

There are hundreds of different ideas about the causes and treatment of depression. Be it for good or bad, modern medicine will not accept any theories unless they are evidence based. It concerns me that there are people who jeopardise their emotional and physical health by partaking in alternative treatments that have no scientific basis.

All psychiatrists should be supportive of their patients and understand that people with depression need a lot more from their doctor than just a reassuring pat on the back and a prescription. While most people who are referred to me require antidepressant treatment, I try and help them deal with difficult issues in their life by encouraging them to talk about relationships or work difficulties. I will recommend psychotherapy, even intense psychotherapy, if I think they need it.

I believe there is an important role for exercise in the treatment of depression and I prescribe exercise to all my patients. I feel so strongly about this that I basically make exercise a mandatory part of treatment. There are studies showing that for some people exercise can be as effective as antidepressants. I recommend that my patients build up to forty minutes of exercise four times a week. I suggest brisk walking, not power walking or jogging, so that age should not be a deterrent for taking up an exercise program. The added bonus of exercise is that it is good for general health and can help prevent some illnesses: for example, disorders of the bowel are less frequent in people who exercise.

About 50 per cent of people who qualify as having major depression either don't know they have it or do nothing about it. They are aware that they are unhappy but they blame it on circumstances. About 50 per cent of people who do see a doctor for depression do not get antidepressants, and among those who do, at least half won't get adequate doses.

A recommended dose of antidepressants may be effective for one person and not for another. People have different metabolisms and react differently to the same drug. Some people have side-effects from certain antidepressants and others will experience no side-effects at all. I am very meticulous in trying to establish the right dose of the right antidepressant for each individual.

There is no clear-cut explanation as to why people respond so differently to different treatments for their depressive illness. It is very important that every person presenting with depression be treated as an individual. I cannot stress this enough. I believe it is an important part of the recovery process that each patient knows they are being treated in a way that has been tailored for their individual needs. Constant monitoring is important in the early stages of treatment so that all changes and responses can be evaluated.

Two-thirds of patients will experience an improvement with the first antidepressant I prescribe. If a patient does not respond to the first or second type of antidepressant drug, I see the depression as 'treatment-resistant' and will pursue other options, including electroconvulsive therapy (ECT), lithium or hospitalisation (particularly if there is a suicide risk).

Some people still hold erroneous views on ECT. It gained a terrible reputation after the movie *One Flew Over the Cuckoo's Nest* in which ECT was depicted as a horrendous and painful experience. In fact ECT is quite painless and while we still don't understand exactly why it works, it can be a very successful form of treatment for many people.

I don't think it is a good idea for lists of antidepressants to be included in a book of this nature because there are so many different ones on the market and it can become very confusing for the non-medical person to understand or appreciate their various functions.

No one should consider taking antidepressants without consulting a doctor. I cannot make this point too strongly.

The general practitioner

Dr Kath Dunne, MBBS, FRACGP, DipHyp, is a general practitioner in a women's clinic in an inner city suburb. Her patients include professional and working women, stay-at-home mothers, and students. She talks about the difficulty in getting some of her patients to come to terms with what is clearly a depressive illness. She is concerned that so many patients find it difficult or embarrassing to broach the subject of their emotional health. She stresses that it is important

for a patient to have a trusting relationship with their GP and if they cannot establish such a relationship they should, if possible, find another doctor with whom they feel more comfortable.

My priority when seeing a patient for the first time is to try to establish a good rapport and open communication. It is vital that people feel they can talk to you and that you will not be judgemental or dismissive. This applies to both emotional and physical problems. Once you have established a trusting and mutually respectful relationship with your patient you are in a position to be more effective and supportive.

I have a number of patients who come to me with symptoms that in reality are masked depression. A proportion of these patients will actually know they are suffering from depression but will not mention it. Often depression is not mentioned until I bring it up or they are about to leave. It concerns me that so many people still find it hard to accept that they are feeling depressed.

The various forms of depression can present in many ways and I try to ask questions that will give me some insight into my patients' emotional as well as physical conditions. I set out to ask probing questions in a nonjudgemental way, as some patients can become very defensive and close up completely if you indicate they may be suffering from a mental health or emotional problem.

Some patients are so uptight about the label 'mental health problem' that they will try and avoid discussing it with me. This makes it very hard to treat them effectively. I wish they would realise that masking their true feelings only delays appropriate treatment and a good outcome. I try and maintain eye contact when I sense a patient is avoiding the real issue, and if they avoid eye contact I know that they are not comfortable about some aspect of their health. Of course, depression is not the only issue that people can feel uncomfortable discussing. I believe that it is usually possible to treat most forms of depression effectively if you can detect it early. The earlier the detection, the quicker the treatment and recovery.

Examples of the types of comments that suggest a state of masked depression are: 'I feel constantly tired', 'I feel angry', 'My libido is way down', 'I feel constantly agitated', 'I hardly sleep.'

I rarely start treatment for depression until I feel that I have a clear understanding of a patient's problems and needs. Once I suspect depression in a patient I ask myself a number of questions, including:

- How severe is the depression?
- Are they coping okay or are they just putting on a brave face?
- Are they in danger of destructive behaviour or attempted suicide?
- Do they have a support structure?
- Can treatment be delayed for a week or two while together we try to sort out the appropriate treatment, or is immediate intervention required?

Working towards getting the correct treatment for depression is a collaborative exercise between the patient and myself. For example, I don't want to just write out a prescription for a patient who has a resistance to taking medication as it would be a pointless exercise.

Once I have answers to these questions I try to help the patient identify how their depression is manifesting and what may be causing it. I try to identify if it is a reactive depression or a major depression.

Some of my younger patients who are only in their early twenties are presenting with depression. A problem that many of them talk about is the pressure at work. I think there is a rise in work-related stress and this is a real concern. Some of the hours these young women are expected to work are crazy. I suggest that they learn some relaxation techniques and make time for activities such as walking or sport. I can only suggest that people make lifestyle changes – people have to want to make them and unfortunately many find this hard. I believe that certain lifestyle factors (lack of exercise, poor nutrition and excessive alcohol consumption) can aggravate depression or depressive symptoms. I believe that some type of exercise is very important, but unfortunately as depressive symptoms increase people tend to lose the motivation to maintain a healthy lifestyle.

I refer my patients on to a psychologist or psychiatrist if I believe that they will benefit from more specialised attention. I never let a person I suspect of having depression just go away and deal with it on her own.

I cannot stress enough how important it is to start treating depression as soon as possible. Untreated depression can quickly get worse. People must understand that it is important to seek advice and treatment as soon as they can.

The psychologist

Phil Blackwood is a psychologist whose practice covers a large region in rural Australia. He brings to our attention many of the issues that confront country people and are contributing to unprecedented levels of depression in rural Australia.

Rural areas in many parts of Australia are doing it tough. Lots of country people are really struggling. I see towns with empty shops and few public facilities. Some towns have little or no services at all. Once the banks started pulling out, other businesses were forced to follow. There are few support groups for people who have emotional problems. Most country GPs are overworked and simply don't have the time to adequately help those with mental health issues. Some country people have to travel long distances for everything, including health care.

In the course of my work I am exposed to an enormous amount of depression and anxiety. People are worried about global issues but the most pressing issues concern their quality of life.

Country people are amazingly stoic and generally very shy when talking about emotional issues. They are also very sensitive about how they are perceived. I have to arrange to see some people out of hours because they don't want to be seen having an appointment with me. If you are a fourth- or fifth-generation farmer it can be seen as a great failure to admit that things are not going too well.

There are major levels of depression among farmers and small businesspeople in rural Australia but unfortunately many of these people still equate depression with weakness. Because of this perception they often don't seek help until they reach crisis point. The loss of status when the farm is struggling can be very hard to bear. I have seen families living on cereal for weeks because they are too proud to accept any help.

However, the community spirit in the country is fantastic. People really support each other when they are made aware that someone needs help. I am touched by the many genuine acts of human kindness that I witness among country people.

I avoid a presumptive or didactic approach with individuals who see me. It is so important to get across that their emotional condition is not due to personal failure or weakness.

I am particularly concerned about young people in rural areas because often there is simply nothing for them to do in their spare time if they are not involved in an organised sport. Sport is often one of the few activities available in some towns. Unemployment is also a major issue with country kids. So many of the young people I see are facing a bleak and difficult future and they know it. It is tempting to turn to drink or drugs to alleviate boredom and a sense of hopelessness.

In my experience, the police in the country are often very supportive when dealing with young lawbreakers, many of whom have depression and other mental health problems. Many police show great compassion, often advocating for the young people to be given another chance rather than getting a gaol sentence. The police have a very important role in helping combat youth depression in the bush and don't receive enough recognition or praise for what they do.

The suicide rate among young men living in rural Australia is tragically high. Adolescence can be a time for impulsive and high-risk behaviour, and occasionally a transient depressed mood can result in a completed suicide. Suicidal thinking and depression in the elderly also seems under-recognised as it can sometimes be 'masked' by bereavement and/or health problems.

I regularly organise gatherings in country towns for the local people, where I outline the symptoms of depression. It is concerning that so many people have no idea what depression is or how to treat it. I have large numbers of clients who have only come to see me after they have reached rock-bottom. Most don't suspect they have depression even though they are telling me how lousy they feel. It is still very hard for many people to accept that they may have a mental illness. Men in particular find it hard to talk about emotional problems. Many men in rural Australia become socially isolated and have no one to talk to. Women seem to be better at talking about their feelings in a more open manner.

Sadly I am not in a position to change the economic and social problems experienced by many country Australians, though I am convinced that much of the depression in rural areas is in part attributable to deprivation of community facilities, loneliness, isolation and unemployment.

It is very hard for me to tell someone that they must try to relax and be more positive about their life when I know they are experiencing chronic financial stress. Some people who need assistance have to wait days or even weeks before they can get help in the public system because there is no way they can afford a private consultation with a psychologist or psychiatrist. The government and the community as a whole must work together to address these problems or the levels of depression in rural areas will continue to rise.

CHAPTER SIX

FOOD AND CHEMICAL INTOLERANCE

This chapter was written by Sue Dengate, a psychology graduate and former high-school teacher whose interest in food
intolerance dates from the birth of her first child. She is the
author of several bestselling books, including *Fed Up* and *The
Failsafe Cookbook*, and has published research concerning
the behavioural effects of a common bread preservative. Sue
and her husband, Dr Howard Dengate, a food scientist, run
the Food Intolerance Network through their website (www.
fedupwithfoodadditives.info).

Food and chemical intolerance is not normally associated
with depression in mainstream medical literature but recent
research clearly demonstrates that it can be a contributing
factor in causing depressive symptoms for some people.

Depression and hyperactivity can be two sides of the same coin. My
interest in the effects of food on behaviour began with hyperactive
children. My daughter had been diagnosed with attention deficit hyperactivity disorder (ADHD) and had improved remarkably on a low-chemical
elimination diet, which limits consumption of food additives as well as
natural food chemicals called salicylates and amines. After this success,
I began a support network for other families trialling the diet, which I call
'failsafe', a rather clumsy acronym for 'free of additives and low in salicylates, amines and flavour enhancers'.

One day a father I'll call Richard decided to test for an allergic reaction
to amines by eating chocolate and bananas. He had expected no effect.
'How wrong can you get!' he wrote.

I had a violent reaction within a few hours and have never felt so awful in all my life. Here are some of the symptoms: depression, suicidal tendencies (not just thoughts), melancholy, looking for an argument, feeling the whole world was against me, lethargy, shakes, pressure on the skull and tingling in the extremities, feeling hung-over, unable to focus on thoughts, ringing in the ears, insomnia. The hung-over feeling lasted until the next day.

Although Richard had suffered from episodes of depression for many years, he had followed the diet only to support his son who had begun the diet after being diagnosed with ADHD. Richard was pleased to discover his depression was related to foods, and once he knew which foods affected him, he was happy to avoid former favourites. Richard's story was the first of hundreds of similar stories received by the Food Intolerance Network.

Amines

Amines, such as tyramine in cheese and phenylethylamine in chocolate, are chemicals produced by the breakdown of proteins and are commonly related to migraine. Foods that contain enough amines to contribute to problems in some people includes tomatoes, avocados, tinned fish, prawns, citrus fruits, grapes and processed meats such as ham.

Unlike allergic reactions, which are a rapid response to proteins in a few foods, food intolerance reactions can be delayed for hours or even days, and can build up from similar chemicals in many different foods, so people who are affected by food chemicals rarely realise which ones are affecting them.

A woman I'll call Rose is a typical example. Rose experienced her first episodes of depression while at university. She confessed that her 'drug of choice' whenever she was under stress was chocolate. She would eat up to a block a day but it wasn't until she went failsafe many years later that tests revealed the amines in chocolate had been the cause of her problems.

I felt awful, didn't want to get out of bed, couldn't be bothered with anything and was sure everyone hated me. Anything anyone said was taken the wrong way and I nearly chucked in the job that I sometimes really enjoy. I spent hours telling my husband about how terrible my life was and analysing everything in detail trying to work out why everyone hated me. I had increasing suicidal thoughts, thinking through what was in the house to help me. Thank goodness I never got to the stage of actually doing anything about it.

Like Richard, Rose now avoids the foods that affect her. She says, 'When I am strictly failsafe, I feel happier and am nicer to be around. I enjoy life and have lots of energy instead of lying around like a half-comatose couch potato.'

Amines are not the only food chemical involved in depression. People are affected differently, which is why a low-chemical elimination diet is necessary to test for individual food sensitivities.

Salicylates

Salicylates are among the more than 100 different chemicals in produce such as strawberries and potatoes. Humans are used to thinking of fruit and vegetables as the healthiest foods, but plants contain chemicals such as salicylates to protect themselves from insects and diseases. In sensitive people or in big doses, some of these chemicals can cause unwanted side-effects. Eating is like walking a chemical tightrope where we have to balance the advantages of the nutrients against the disadvantages of eating natural pesticides. Doses of salicylates are increasing in our food supply due to food-processing techniques such as juicing, which concentrate the salicylates, and the development of fruit and vegetables designed to be picked unripe – when salicylates are at their highest – for longer shelf life.

Since salicylate reactions build up slowly, people with salicylate sensitivity never realise what their problem is until they do an elimination diet. As one mother said, 'I felt a bit like Saul when he had his revelation on the road to Damascus. I didn't even think that my son's behavioural symptoms could be caused by food. Now I've been eliminating, I can see why. Most of his reactions are delayed by at least a day, if not two.'

Several years ago, a medical journal reported the case of a twenty-seven-year-old university graduate whose severe depressive episodes had not responded to a range of psychotropic drugs. The patient, from a stable and caring family, had a history of motor tics, generalised anxiety, social phobia, panic attacks and obsessive-compulsive disorder (manifested mainly in checking compulsions), as well as gastrointestinal and other symptoms. After four weeks on a low-chemical elimination diet, the patient's mood and other symptoms improved considerably. Testing revealed that he was severely affected by salicylates as well as other food chemicals. While staying on the diet, the patient was able to remain symptom free, and when reviewed after a year had been able to return to full-time work.

Many of our members have reported similar sensitivity to salicylates. One woman who had always been prone to food cravings woke up in a psychiatric ward with slashed wrists after a three-day binge on canned pineapple. She had no memory of what had happened. 'I get so impulsive, I don't know what I'm doing,' she explained. Through elimination and testing she discovered that salicylates, which occur abundantly in pineapple, were associated with both her food cravings and mood swings.

Other foods

Members of our network have also reported effects from wheat, gluten or dairy products. A loving mother of two children described how she 'couldn't stop thinking about terrible things that might happen to my kids'. It never occurred to her that diet might help with these problems, yet when the family became failsafe to help with the son's inattention, the mother's irrational fears turned out to be related to both salicylates and gluten. She was even more surprised to find that her children were also affected, with social withdrawal as well as irrational fears.

Individual tolerance to food chemicals depends on a combination of genetic and environmental factors. A family history of migraine, irritable bowel symptoms, sleep disturbance or behavioural problems such as ADHD can all be indications of susceptibility. Factors that may increase vulnerability to food intolerance include stress, lack of sleep, illness, exposure to toxic chemicals or medications, age and hormonal fluctuations.

Women are more food sensitive while premenstrual, during their childbearing years and after giving birth. A young mother I'll call Jenny had always had horrible periods. She described herself as 'a chronic bitch for two weeks out of every month', suffering severe cramping, heavy bleeding and frequent clots. Then she had her first child:

> Straight after my son's birth I knew something was wrong. When I got home I just sat in bed staring into space. I couldn't get out of bed, couldn't do anything, couldn't sleep. I would start panicking when I heard the baby cry. My mother had to come and look after us, doing all the work and bringing my son to me for feeds.

When her second child was born, the same thing happened. This time, however, when her baby was four months old Jenny started a low-chemical elimination diet to help her breastfed baby's eczema. 'I felt better than I had for months', Jenny recalled. However, after weaning the baby, Jenny went back to her normal diet and again started feeling anxious, overwhelmed and unable to sleep despite antidepressants. She knows now she needed to go back on the diet but it seemed too hard. 'I was in denial. For me, giving up chocolate was a really big thing.'

It took Jenny eighteen failsafe months to wean herself off antidepressants. During that time her premenstrual syndrome (PMS), other menstrual problems and depression all disappeared and tests showed that she was sensitive to 'nearly everything'.

> If someone had told me when I first got postnatal depression that my problems were due to food intolerance, I would have gone on the diet straight away. I've been on this diet so long now that I can't really remember what it's like to be depressed.

Jenny's story illustrates how difficult it is for most people to cut out their favourite foods, even with evidence that it may bring them remarkable relief. People are especially reluctant to give up salicylates. I am constantly amazed at how many are prepared to go through years of hell, spending thousands of dollars searching for a cure just because they are not prepared to give up that last orange a day or some other salicylate-containing food.

Food additives

People sensitive to salicylates and amines are likely to be affected by food additives that have similar effects. These include artificial colours, one natural colour known as annatto 160b, artificial flavours, flavour enhancers and preservatives.

Unfortunately, it is easy to eat additives inadvertently. Consumers are often unaware of additives in restaurant foods or in foods where unlisted additives are permitted. Anti-oxidants such as BHA (320), which is used to preserve vegetable oils, are the most difficult to avoid. One failsafe mother described how her highly sensitive teenager tried to hang himself after eating unlabelled BHA. Another failsafe teenager experienced months of depression due to unlisted BHA in blended butter. 'I was exhausted all the time', she said. 'I felt my life was worthless and that I would be better off dead.' Although for most consumers a single dose is not enough to cause problems, effects are cumulative and can build up slowly.

Food intolerance in children

Young children can be affected too. An anxious seven-year-old with learning difficulties improved so much during a three-week elimination diet that as a reward his mother offered him anything he wanted in the supermarket. He chose an icy-pole with seven artificial colours, BHA and artificial flavours. There was no reaction for the first two days and then on day three, the family saw a massive 'bad and sad' reaction. First, the boy 'turned into a monster' and no one wanted to have anything to do with him. Then he sank into a deep, dark depression. He wanted to hurt himself, he wanted to be dead. As his mother said, 'It was awful and so dramatic. He was aware of what caused the reaction and never wants to eat one again.' Yet this family, like so many others, had never noticed any effects of foods, because when problematic food chemicals are eaten every day, ill-effects appear to fluctuate with no obvious cause.

Another family, eating only failsafe foods, discovered that their eight-year-old daughter's depression was linked to amines. After two years being failsafe, the mother wrote:

> Pre-failsafe she was mildly depressed, as well as lethargic, pale, anxious, dizzy and 'spacy'. Her amine challenge resulted in severe depression, including bouts of suicidal thoughts and almost psychotic agitation. Based on pre-diet behaviours, she had been classified as having a highly anxious temperament. A number of health professionals have told us they expect to see her back during her teenage years, expecting her to need anti-depressants. However, after two years failsafe she shows no signs of mental illness in any form and no longer seems a candidate for anxiety and depression.

Fumes and perfumes

It's hard enough for people to understand that they can be affected by salicylates they eat, but salicylates can also be absorbed through the skin and inhaled in strong odours. Salicylates are synthesised for use in many artificial flavours and perfumes – which are essentially the same chemicals. Since the strong fruit, flower, pine, eucalyptus or chemical smells of toiletries, perfumes, air fresheners, household cleaners and medications can cause ill-effects, failsafers avoid strong smells.

Perfumes and other chemicals that become gases at room temperature (such as solvents and pesticides) are known as volatile organic compounds (VOCs). Some VOCs cause the characteristic 'new' smell of buildings, furniture and cars that is associated with 'sick building syndrome', the symptoms of which include eye, skin and throat irrita-tion, headaches, lethargy, dizziness, nausea and memory disturbance.

A study in England found that one in ten farmers regularly exposed to organophosphate pesticides suffer from symptoms ranging from extreme tiredness to suicidal impulses. But you don't have to be a farmer to be exposed to such chemicals. Organophosphates used as flame retardants find their way into our houses and offices in a range of products including computer components and the foam filling in sofas and other soft furnishings. When the trisphosphate flame retardant TCPP was tested on thousands of laboratory rats, four studies out of nine listed 'depression' as the main clinical sign, while the others listed hunched posture and lethargy.

Most people are unlikely to be able to identify organophosphates as the cause of their depression, and children are even more vulnerable as few families would go to the trouble of exchanging new furniture for natural futons or eco-friendly computers just because their children said they didn't like the smell. A low-chemical elimination diet assists sensi-tive people to identify the effects of both foods and environmental chemicals on their health and moods.

People with depression who would like to try a low-chemical elimina-tion diet for their symptoms need to be aware that they may suffer a recurrence of their symptoms during the first two weeks due to with-drawal, and that they may experience major reactions during testing. For this reason, anyone attempting a low-chemical elimination diet should be supervised by a health professional. The Food Intolerance Network provides a list of failsafe-friendly dieticians and psychologists. There is more information on the website (www.fedupwithfoodaddi tives.info).

CHAPTER SEVEN

LISTENING TO DEPRESSION

The following stories are from a diverse group of people who have all suffered depression. Their experiences are individual, diverse and at times heartbreaking, and yet all of these people have forged for themselves meaningful and rewarding lives after some stupendous battles with depression. For some the battle continues.

Robert Bourke

Robert is a company director in his mid-forties. After some years of treatment-resistant depression he is responding well to transcranial magnetic stimulation (TMS). While he now feels much better, he continues to suffer guilt and anxiety about how his long-term depression may have irrevocably damaged his marriage.

Depression is nearly impossible to describe. I like to think that I am an intelligent and rational person and that I have achieved a lot professionally. Yet when I sink into depression I lose all sense of self and of my place in life. I can say to you now, while I am well, that if I have another depressive episode I know I will get through it, but when I am sunk in depression I have no sense of it ever leaving me. It is like a horrible, suffocating fog that is impossible to find a way through. Only those who have suffered major depression could possibly imagine how utterly devastating it is. While I am not depressed at the moment, I am suffering moments of dread about another episode creeping up on me. That is what happens to me, it just creeps up on me and I know I am about to go to hell.

My current treatment is the first treatment I have had that has given me some hope, hope for a life without the depression monster always in wait. I dream of complete recovery but would be happy for longer periods between bouts.

There is a lack of certainty in life when you are depressed. You wonder just how long the people supporting you are going to put up with all the pain and drama. I cannot bear to think what it must be like to be alone and depressed. I have always had the love and support of my family, but of course, when you are depressed no amount of love or support is enough to make you feel better. I don't even feel grateful for their help. I am totally absorbed in my depression and am unable to put myself in another's position. I know I am really awful to live with when I am down, but I also know that when I come out of depression I am not an uncaring, selfish person. I do worry, however, that eventually my wife will leave me. Is there a limit to how long love can last when one party has regular depressive episodes? This worry haunts me when I am not depressed, even though my wife assures me that she will always stick by me. So even when I am not depressed, bloody depression still has a hold on me. I need to change my thought patterns and try to become more positive and optimistic now I am feeling so much better.

I am about to have some cognitive behavioural therapy to help me change my thinking and to become more positive about my future and my marriage. I had tried therapy before but was so depressed and negative that it did not help. I was simply too ill to respond.

Unfortunately, I have tried three different types of antidepressants in the past, including Prozac, and have had a terrible reaction to each one. I really thought I was going mad on Prozac, because I actually felt worse. It made me feel very angry and aggressive.

I call my depression the 'black bastard' and yet for the first time I am optimistic that I may have the black bastard on the run. For me the TMS treatment has been miraculous.

Helen Reynolds

Helen and her twin sister, Ruth, were best friends. When Ruth died unexpectedly in her forties from complications after surgery, Helen developed major depression.

I am glad to have the opportunity to write about this experience rather than talk about it. This way I won't get sidetracked and include aspects that are important to me in the understanding of the whole experience but are not necessary in terms of speaking about the depression I experienced following her death.

Ruth and I spoke to each other at least once a day, every day. We would often dial each other's number simultaneously; our sense of humour and musical tastes were identical. We would turn to each other at precisely the same moment when a common nerve was struck. If I ever had a concern or a cause for unhappiness, she always made me feel better as she completely understood my pain and my perspective. There was never the need to explain. We were on the same side! I suspect only twins can fully grasp the significance of that oneness.

Four months after she died I hit rock-bottom. The desolation and fear were indescribable. I cried in the shower, I wailed in the car, I couldn't make decisions; I didn't want to talk to anyone, or anyone to talk to me. My grief and the grief of Ruth's husband and children overwhelmed me. I felt guilty about the impact my emotional state was having on my own children. There was also the grief of our parents and siblings. I wanted to put all our lives on fast forward so that time would pass quickly and we would all be dead. The only thing that would have helped me was impossible to have. For the first time in my life I felt that I was on my own. My GP realised I needed help and referred me to a psychiatrist named Jo, and she was wonderful. I was medicated for approximately three years and saw Jo regularly. She pushed me over the hump, and my husband and children waited patiently for me to return. Now I am healed, though I will miss Ruth for the rest of my life.

Salma Makhlouf

Salma came to Australia ten years ago with her husband and two children to join a close-knit community of family and friends in a Sydney suburb. Salma teaches part time in an Islamic school and her husband is a practising GP. The family are happily integrated into the wider community and have many Australian friends. They have had two more children since coming to Australia. Salma developed severe depression after experiencing discrimination and harassment after the events of 11 September 2001.

After the planes flew into the towers in New York my life changed. We watched the television that day and we were all so upset. It was a horrible and crazy thing and all good Muslims were horrified and sad. Later that day I took the two youngest children for a walk to the shops and a group of young men passing in a car screamed out abuse, 'Muslims are murderers, go home.' The children were scared, as they had never heard anything like that said before. On the way back two women passed us on the pavement and one of them spat and said, 'Mad killers.' When I got home I could not stop crying, it was so horrible.

Our Muslim friends were all upset and very angry at what had happened but they did not cry all the time like I did. I felt afraid for my family and for Muslims in Australia and in other western countries. I could not sleep and I could not eat. My husband was very worried about me as I would not leave the house. I know it was an overreaction but I could not stop it – this is what happened to me. Other Muslim friends were abused in the street. One Australian friend came over with flowers to try to make me feel better but her kindness made me cry more. I shall never forget how kind our Australian friends were after that time. They did not stop our friendship because we are Muslim.

After a few months my husband took me to one of the doctors in the surgery where he works and she told me I was depressed. My husband did not want to see me as a doctor because he said he did not understand depression. The other doctor told me I must try to go out and see friends and talk about my feelings. She told me to try and do some fast walking every day to help me feel better. Nothing helped. I was put on tablets. At first this was upsetting for my husband as he believed I should be able to get better without drugs. He and the other doctor then decided it was the only way to treat my depression. I was on Avanza for three years and in that time I improved very much. I am much better but I still become very upset with the killing and fighting in the world. Muslims are good people and I need Australians to know that. I hope I will not need drugs again but sometimes I feel the great tears coming on and I try and hold them back so my family won't worry about me.

Janet De Silva

Janet is sixty-seven years old. She retired as a headmistress at sixty-five and says that she misses the satisfaction that came with her job. Her husband died three years ago after a long and happy marriage. She has one adult daughter. Her GP believes her depression started soon after her retirement and is encouraging her to take up some activities outside the home that will involve interaction with other people. Her daughter believes the depression started soon after Janet was widowed. Janet thinks it is a combination of these and many other life issues and is particularly worried about her over-sensitivity to world events.

Depression has the ability to change my sense of who I am and my perception of how others see me. Depression is a monster; everything becomes false and my mind is blurred to reality. I was diagnosed with depression a year ago and am still pretty bad. I tried therapy with a psychologist for a few months first but when nothing seemed to improve I went to see a psychiatrist.

Once I was a confident and easygoing person. I was capable of talking about my life on quite a personal level and enjoyed a large group of friends. I could easily discuss illnesses that invaded the organs of my body but have found it extremely difficult to discuss the illness that has invaded my mind.

I am currently receiving biological treatment. I am on an antidepressant called Zoloft and I have improved slightly over a two-month period. I sincerely hope that the improvement continues.

I think that my up-and-down moods are a result of a genetic predisposition that is exacerbated by life events and my reaction to these events. My mother had depression, although it was not diagnosed until she was well into her fifties. I remember her staying in bed a lot and my father making excuses for her. As children we were told she had bad headaches.

I am finding it very difficult to come to terms with the world we live in – there seems to be pain and misery everywhere. I become very distressed at some of the images we see on television and have decided I should not watch the news any more. I noticed this strong reaction began when I saw some terrible scenes of the carnage in East Timor a few years ago. I found the images profoundly disturbing, especially images of children's bodies. I had to stop myself watching any of the images from the terrible tsunami in South-East Asia. I felt almost suicidal just hearing about it on the radio.

Maybe it has something to do with becoming older and realising that my time on Earth is limited, but I was once able to cope with the external world and while I always hated violence I was able to enjoy my own life.

I think my moods are a response to a variety of life changes and the realisation that as I age my options are becoming limited. I am finding getting old rather difficult. I'm not worried about looking older as I have never been vain but I do worry about becoming a frail, dependent old lady. Things like bladder control and energy levels are simply not what they used to be. That might be at the heart of my problem. Very little in my life is as it used to be. Still I do find it very distressing that I have sunk so low emotionally. I suppose you could say I feel ashamed that I have depression.

Roger Hooper

Roger developed severe depressive symptoms just after he completed Year 11 at school. His results were good and he was looking forward to a carefree summer holiday. Then he started to feel awful. After reading about a champion AFL footballer having depression, Roger decided to seek medical help.

It was insidious to begin with. I guess the symptoms sort of crept up on me. I thought I had some sort of virus. I felt great lethargy and had not a scrap of energy. I started having really horrible and negative thoughts about life and myself in general. I felt many emotions that I had not experienced before. I was angry, sad, scared, aggressive and weepy, and all I really wanted to do was sleep. I tried to be normal, particularly with my friends, but it became impossible. I did not go back to school when term started in 2004. I was now a dropout. My parents were freaked and did their best to be supportive but I told them to get lost. I was totally ungrateful for their concern, even though I knew something was wrong. When my mother suggested I could be depressed I slammed the door in her face.

What made me sit up and realise that maybe I was depressed was when I read about Nathan Thompson in the paper and then heard him interviewed on radio. What he described about his depression could have been me with a few exceptions – I don't think Nathan was rude to people when he was down.

I went to a doctor and I was diagnosed with depression. I was put on medication and within six months I was back to normal. I have gone back to do my final year at school – I missed a year but no one has made me feel like an idiot. I see my doctor regularly and we are talking together about me going off medication in a few months. I thought I might write Nathan a letter of thanks. God knows what I would be like if his story had not given me the guts to face up to the fact that I was really ill. I have already bought my mother a giant bunch of flowers as a way of saying sorry. I was a horrible person for six months but the family never deserted me.

Amanda's story

Amanda is twenty-five years old and has suffered from depression for more than five years. So far she has not experienced significant relief from any of the treatments offered by her doctors.

Unless you have experienced depression yourself it is very hard to explain the feeling this illness brings. I will attempt to explain how it 'feels' to live with depression instead of what it 'physically' does. In my opinion there are two types of depression. There is the feeling of being depressed that everyone at some stage experiences, for example, if you lose a loved one and don't know how to go on living without them. Then there is 'clinical' depression, a chemical imbalance in the nervous system. It is something completely out of your control. I have the latter. If you truly want to understand depression, please take the time to think about the following and try to apply it to feelings you have experienced in your life.

Think back to a time when you felt low.

Think back to a time when you felt very lonely.

Think back to a time when you felt so overwhelmed with sadness and regret that you couldn't think of anything else.

Think back to a time of utter despair.

Now imagine having those feelings all at once, twenty-four hours a day, seven days a week, all on top of daily life, whether that involves a stressful job, young children noisily running around under your feet, or an argument with a loved one. If you can imagine all these emotions at the same time, you will begin to understand how it can be hard to get out of bed in the morning – how going to the local supermarket for groceries seems like it would take ten times the energy that you have. You feel totally drained both physically and mentally. This is the world of depression.

Leslie Kingsley

Leslie is an artist living in Tasmania.

I am basically restarting my painting business from scratch. Actually, I am currently kick-starting my whole existence, from rock-bottom up. As I believe bedrock to be an excellent basis for a new foundation, I am full of optimism. I know how debilitating depression can be if it is allowed to hijack our time and emotions. I have never enjoyed it. I used to despise the way it invaded like a thick, invisible smoke – suddenly there in all its choking power.

Depression makes little inanimate innocents like a light switch take on the appearance of something hateful. A favourite ornament becomes cloaked with all that is loathsome, and a beautiful clump of trees on the horizon that usually lifts the heart becomes a sight so empty of joy that I cannot even look at it.

I believe that fighting depression can teach us much about ourselves. I have dedicated time to discovering how to extricate myself from depression quickly and effectively. Although I have had a taste of the company of the black beast, I am basically a happy person. In fact I make a deliberate habit of being happy.

I understand some sufferers of depression can use their affliction to manipulative ends. On the two or three occasions I have been submerged and dangerously imprisoned by an undertow of grey emotions, I did not know what was happening at the time. Had someone tried to tell me I was depressed, I would have thought them absurd. I didn't feel sad. I have known great sadness. I was not sad. I could not understand what I was feeling. It was only after I had constructed, and effectively used, the mental tools I needed to disentangle myself that I understood I had indeed been severely depressed.

I found that the more quickly I could identify the curtain as it descended, the more readily I could employ my tools to rise above it. This required considerable mental discipline coupled with deep feeling (heart and mind, I guess), both directed at the same goal. I don't know if this would work with every kind of depression. I have been told that some forms are caused by a chemical imbalance. I believe, however, that someone afflicted by a great sadness will have their chemical makeup altered. So, which comes first – the chemical chicken or the emotional egg?

The ancients used to refer to Earth as 'the schoolroom' – we are all here for a time to learn and to contribute to the knowledge of others. I consider every person or situation to be a potential teacher. If only we could hear the lesson behind the words, the message disguised by the actions or the understanding hidden beneath the stress of a situation, then we would add to the greater part of ourselves and not berate fate for our imagined misfortune.

Daniel Rose

Daniel, aged forty-seven, works as a successful freelance graphic artist from a studio at his home. After his marriage broke up he says he fell apart. He took drugs (heroin and marijuana) over a fourteen-month period and attempted suicide twice during that time. Previously he had only used marijuana very occasionally for relaxation. He says he owes his life to the care and support of a GP who diagnosed depression and admitted him to hospital. He is now drug free and working full time while undertaking cognitive behavioural therapy (CBT) twice a week. He was on antidepressants for a year after promising his doctor he would stay off the recreational drugs.

I was separated from my wife and children. It was not an acrimonious break-up but I was very upset about not seeing my children every day. I have always worked from home and, except for contact with my family, I am a bit of a loner. My wife was the one who had lots of friends and a full life outside the house. I tended to pursue solitary activities such as reading and listening to music. I never missed people when living with the family.

When I realised I was in some sort of emotional trouble I was unable to ask anyone for help. I now realise I did not know how or where to ask for help. I did not see myself as the sort of person who would join a support group to work through my feelings of loneliness, or any other feelings for that matter. Deep down I rather despised people who let it all hang out and had never talked about my emotions to anyone.

When the family left I felt very alone. I started using drugs as an emotional and spiritual analgesic – it was an appalling life decision. I was so out of it most of the time, I could not have found my way out of a children's playground. I started to drink quite a bit of red wine and was not eating properly. I'd pull myself together when I knew the children were coming over, but they picked it in one that something was not right. I am told that physically I looked bloody awful.

I became increasingly isolated and while I still managed to work for a few hours each day I was aware that my work was suffering. I simply did not care about anything and what I produced was not up to my usual rather exacting standard.

My wife and the children seemed to be thriving without me. Both children were doing well at uni and my wife was completing a degree. I heard that she had met another man. I felt very, very sad and I am ashamed to say I started thinking that they would all be better off without me. I was also very ashamed about the drug-taking.

Suicide became a natural option for me because I could see no way out of my problems. I really hated my life. When my head was clear I despised myself for using drugs to get through the day. I went to four or five doctors in different suburbs and used a false name twice. This made me feel like a real criminal. I complained of insomnia and got scripts for sleeping tablets, and eventually I tried to commit suicide with an overdose. I did not succeed because I had no idea what dose was required and did not take enough. I woke up feeling awful, but I was alive. And I was briefly pleased to be alive.

However, I tried again and this time my son, who had called in by chance, found me unconscious. This caused awful drama and pain and I am extraordinarily lucky to be alive and to have suffered no brain damage. Two years later I still battle the shame. I am ashamed that my children know I used drugs and tried to kill myself. I am working on getting rid of these feelings as they are completely counterproductive and the kids still love me regardless of my past actions.

This may sound really crazy but I am still in denial about being depressed. I pretend to myself at times that I was not, though I was certainly messed up in the head. I was suffering from unbearable psychological pain and the doctor who finally saved me from myself believes I was severely depressed. I don't want to be labelled as a depressive because it's a hard label to shed. In my view you are either a depressive or a recovered depressive and I don't want to be either. I still have a bit of a way to go before I come to terms with depression and what it did to me.

Jillian Campbell

Jillian is a sixty-year-old married woman who seriously questions the place of placebo treatment in clinical trials. She has suffered from depression since she was a child.

I become very upset and angry when I read comments by some doctors saying that placebos work as well as antidepressants. Why not ask the patients, many of whom would disagree? Why aren't the patients' views even considered? Perhaps some fortunate people do respond to placebos, but I am outraged that some people are not given a chance to make up their own minds and are given placebos when they are obviously in deep distress. My period of hell lasted much longer than necessary because I was given placebos when I was so obviously in need of urgent treatment.

My forty-year history of regular episodes of depression and manic depression began when I was about twelve years old. Over the years psychotherapy helped me cope but did little to alleviate the illness. I was put on a variety of antidepressants, none of which helped. Some made me feel worse, particularly Prozac and Zoloft. I fluctuated from being constantly miserable to desperately depressed. It was a shocking existence both for me and those around me.

Then I was put on amitriptyline and my life changed dramatically. I changed from a suicidal, desperately unhappy person into a happy person. I can finally say that I have a life. I am just so grateful that my husband is still around to once again see the woman he thought he had married. (We met when I was having a relatively benign emotional period.)

The amitriptyline kicked in within a week. I have been stable for two years now and have accepted that I will probably be on it for life. But what a small price to pay for having a life! God knows where I would be if I had been put on a placebo again. I feel so lucky that I found a doctor who took my depression seriously and did not use me as a guinea pig for a medical trial.

Bob Andrews

Bob is an accountant in his mid-fifties. He is rediscovering life after some very hard years battling depression.

It took me over a year to admit that I was depressed. I had had a bad relationship break-up but I thought I was coping okay. By the time I finally saw a doctor I was in a really bad way, yet the doctor still had to convince me that I had depression. I believed it would all pass and that it was a temporary reaction to my life situation.

I found it very hard to get out of bed. This sounds crazy but getting out of bed was a major effort, a really, really major effort. Sometimes I would be lying there for hours trying to get the energy to put a foot out from under the doona. I was very lonely even though I did not want to see people, and to be honest many of my friends did not want to see me. I learnt that even supportive friends don't want you pouring out your misery every time you meet. I have lost friends through my depression. Some of them have not contacted me since I was at my lowest. This hurts but certainly makes me appreciate the few friends who stuck around.

While I don't think group therapy helped me very much at the time, it did make me realise that some people's lives are much worse than mine and I always think about others worse off than myself when I feel my mood slipping down again.

I was in a terrible state and I went to about six doctors before I found one who seemed to understand how ill I was and what a failure I felt.

One doctor I went to was completely cold and robot-like. I told him about my broken romance and I will never forget his comment. He said, 'You have had your screw and now you are paying for it.' It was so insulting and demeaning. I was devastated. It was not his role to make a moral judgement on my private life.

Finally I found a doctor who was supportive, and dare I use such an old-fashioned word as kind. He believed I was a candidate for medication and put me on an antidepressant. I had a terrible reaction – dry mouth, blurred vision, nausea. I also think I became worse. I certainly had suicidal thoughts. I was put on another drug and still did not respond. My GP was very supportive but concerned at my resistance to medication. He told me that some people respond well to exercise. I used to exercise regularly but had let that go when I became depressed. With my doctor's encouragement – no, really his insistence, I suppose – I took up exercise in a big way.

I had to force myself to get out and do it. It was a major effort but I started to do vigorous exercise each day and I quickly noticed an improvement in my emotional state. I believe that exercise releases chemicals in the brain that can lift one's mood. It does not last. You have to keep it up and it has to become a regular part of your life. I chose a bike as my form of exercise and I cycle about 200 kilometres a week. I make sure I go riding at least three times a week. Another bonus of the exercise routine is that I sleep better.

None of this happened overnight. While I steadily improved from when I started exercising, it took nearly three years for me to feel that I had depression under control. I now see my doctor once a month instead of three times a week.

Another issue that my doctor has helped me work out is that alcohol makes me more depressed. While I would get an initial lift, after a few wines I would quickly feel my mood plummet. I was never a heavy drinker but I was a regular drinker. Giving up alcohol has made a huge difference to my emotional state and those days of waking up feeling awful have lessened dramatically. Since I have been exercising regularly I don't miss alcohol. I used to have a wine when I would be feeling a bit flat. Now I go for a bike ride.

Looking back to my childhood I now realise that I used to have lower than normal moods. It was never diagnosed but I think I have probably had a tendency to depression for a long time and a crisis finally tipped me over.

I think I have to accept that I will never be cured of depression but at least I have it firmly under control – days go by without me thinking about it. What is certain is that when I ease off the exercise the depression is there lurking and slowly creeps back.

Robert Taylor

Robert is a sixty-nine-year-old retired judge who enjoys excellent physical health. He started having depressive episodes in his mid-forties following the death of his wife. He has since remarried and his depression has improved over time. He was initially treated with antidepressants and cognitive behavioural therapy, and is a great believer in the benefits of exercise. He had a fairly severe but short-lived depressive episode a year ago, his first for nearly two years. He came through this with the help of therapy and a boost to his exercise program. He is currently feeling confident enough to be off antidepressants but does not discount the possibility of using them again if he has a relapse.

You have to focus on yourself to get through depression. It is not a sin or a crime to concentrate on yourself when you are waging the battle against the big D. I was brought up as a Christian and I guess I am conditioned to feel selfish if I think only of myself. I feel very guilty when I think solely about my own needs, but I know that this is what I have to do when I feel the big D coming down on me.

I used to be embarrassed by the chemist knowing I had depression. There was a really bitchy girl who always seemed to serve me and she would read the script and then give me long judgemental looks before she took it to the pharmacist. I wish she'd stuck to the lipstick counter – this girl had real power over me.

I am sure that my depression was triggered by the death of my wife. She was only forty-three years old and I was absolutely devastated. I had never had a day's depression before her death but I have basically been fighting it on and off ever since. When she died I went into a hole and after a year the GP told me she thought I was depressed. I told her it was natural to feel like this when you have lost the person you love most in the world, so I refused any treatment. I was able to continue working, but in retrospect I was not performing that well. I felt sort of unreal the whole time. It was like watching myself in a play. I felt completely detached from life and just went through the motions. I was able to fool nearly everyone but never myself.

If I had children I suppose it may have been different but there were times when I wanted to die. My religion was useless at this time. In fact I was very angry with God and refused to attend any church services, even though the vicar was a friend and kept asking me. I was actually very, very angry at everything, including myself. It was not a nice place to be.

Genevieve Charles

Genevieve is a thirty-nine-year-old, hard-working secondary teacher who has suffered from recurrent depression for many years. She describes her depression as mild to middling. Her episodes of depression have lessened over the years and she is hopeful that she may become depression-free as time passes.

I have a real problem that is part of my depression. Like everyone else I have low days and blue periods and because of my history of depression I always assume another bout is on the way when I have these moods. But I now realise from experience that a person who suffers from depression can feel low without actually being depressed. I hope this makes sense, but I really need to understand how to differentiate just being down in the dumps from true depression.

Now that my depressive episodes are much less frequent I am beginning to have the confidence to accept some 'down days' without freaking out and thinking I am depressed. This may sound really crazy but I am beginning to believe that you can actually feel depressed for a short time in response to a life event or a health problem and not actually have real depression. I am going to have this discussion with my doctor soon. This realisation is for me a great and wonderful insight. After being a depressive, can you imagine the freedom I will enjoy if I can actually be 'really down' at times and know it is not real depression returning?

Nigel Sinnott

Nigel has suffered from severe, untreatable depression for most of his adult life. The following material originally appeared in *The Skeptic* magazine and Nigel has included a new addendum here.

This is mainly an account of my journey along the long, lonely and gloomy road of depression. I hope that some of it may offer pointers to other people with this mood disorder, particularly to those with hard-to-treat depression.

I have suffered from depression since 1962 for certain, but suspect I have probably had it since 1952, when I was eight years old. So I have had to endure depression for more than forty years. From time to time I hear journalists and glib doctors announce: 'The good news about depression is that it is treatable.' Everything is treatable, even terminal illness, but what matters is whether treatment is effective. By effective I mean bringing about major improvement that is either long lasting or permanent. What is rarely mentioned is that about 6 per cent of depressives do not respond effectively to known methods of treatment.

Drug therapy
Writers and speakers on depression often claim that an antidepressant drug will help about 60 per cent of patients, and that certain types of psychotherapy (particularly CBT) will also have about the same rate of effectiveness.

Antidepressant drugs can, I am sure, help a lot of people, but drugs can also do harm. I went without treatment for years because of doctors and psychiatrists who doled out tricyclic antidepressants to me. The worst hell I know is severe depression compounded by the sedation caused by tricyclic drugs. Other antidepressants can cause anxiety, impaired balance, sexual malfunctioning and raised blood pressure. However, this does not mean that antidepressant drugs are not worth trying.

I first saw a psychiatrist in 1962, but the first time any treatment really helped me was in 1996, when I asked to try moclobemide, if only because it had a side-effect profile I reckoned I could tolerate. Moclobemide raised my mood, but only for about six weeks, and then it packed up rapidly. Fluoxetine worked for about as long, but not nearly as well. Mirtazepine was as good as moclobemide, and lasted longer, but it too packed up after a few months.

Psychotherapy

Psychiatrists vary in their views about whether people with depression should try psychotherapy. Most mental health professionals, however, regard a limited range of psychotherapies as being beneficial for depression. Over the years I have tried group psychotherapy, Freudian psychoanalysis, Jungian psychoanalysis (briefly), hypnotherapy (twice), family therapy and what was supposed to be cognitive therapy. My experience of psychoanalysis changed me from true believer to convinced sceptic. From all these forms of therapy I discovered nothing new or of value about the inner workings of my emotions, but I learnt a fair amount about the thinking and preconceptions of psychotherapists. Yes, I was probably very introspective by temperament, but in some cases I was shocked by the therapist's lack of empathy, imagination and insight.

The last psychotherapist I saw asked me to write down how I hoped my life might differ if I were no longer depressed. I produced a detailed and careful list. The therapist looked at the list and remarked, 'It would have been better if, instead of writing "If I were not depressed I would", you had written "When I am not depressed I will." I realised that this man put a low value on truthfulness; and the more I got to know him, the less trustworthy I found him. He was full of easy slogans and facile promises that lacked substance: his methods were 'all gong, no dinner'.

Electroconvulsive therapy

ECT rarely gets a mention nowadays. This is probably because it was overused and misused in the past for treating depression and a number of other illnesses. It is now used very sparingly, under careful supervision, for certain types of drug-resistant depression, and a qualified anaesthetist has to be present. I tried a course of ECT in 2002. It certainly did not reduce my depression, and it caused short-term memory loss and very high levels of anxiety. The memory loss was sometimes rather farcical, occasionally a bit scary. However, I am glad I was given the chance to try ECT.

Exercise and alcohol

Exercise is often mentioned as good for depression. In my case, however, it generally has the opposite effect: it increases suicidal feelings, often markedly, because when exercising I cannot normally occupy my mind. The things that help me, when very depressed, are writing, reading or watching something engrossing on television. These are partial anodynes or escapes and, of course, as soon as I stop doing them I am fully aware again of the depression.

In recent years evidence has been mounting of a link between depression and heart disease, though the connection may be indirect rather than direct. Depression is often triggered by stress, and depression itself is very stressful. Also some depressives appear to have had childhoods that were more stressful than normal. Chronic stress is an obvious factor in heart disease. Whatever the nature of the link between depression and heart disease, this is further grounds for not neglecting depression.

Mental health professionals regularly warn against the use of alcohol as a form of self-medication for depression. Alcohol may give brief and partial relief from the symptoms, but it certainly does not 'fix' depression, and I am sure that alcohol abuse will exacerbate any mood disorder or mental illness. Nevertheless, I can think of a couple of occasions when moderate alcohol use has probably stopped me attempting suicide, by making me relaxed and sleepy, and dampening down suicidal ideation. However, it is quite possible that alcohol may have the opposite effect on some people with depression.

If I have learnt nothing else in the last forty years, it is that what helps one person with depression may be harmful to someone else. I am aware of the risks of using alcohol too freely, and I decided some years ago (when I started driving regularly) not to drink alcohol earlier than 5.30 p.m. (even on Christmas Day). I also try to limit my consumption to two or three glasses of wine in the evening.

I have also learnt that, in my case, congenial employment correlates (usually) with low levels of depression, and unemployment or uncongenial employment are invariably linked with high levels of depression. I do not think this requires any explanation, but depression has, of course, markedly limited my employment prospects, so I have at times been in something of a vicious circle.

Even as a young man I realised that, unless I could get my depression really under control, my life would be wrecked. Well, I have spent a lot of time, money and effort both on treatment and self-help measures such as major lifestyle changes, but I have to say that I have felt that since 1962 my life has not been worth living.

Bad experiences . . .

I have been less than impressed with a significant minority of mental health professionals I have encountered over the years. One psychiatrist kept me waiting for seven months for group psychotherapy, despite my saying I doubted if it would work because I would feel inhibited in a group. Another psychiatrist told me I did not look very depressed as I was wearing my best suit. (I had a family party to attend afterwards, but I had been feeling suicidal for months.) A third psychiatrist decided I had 'existential depression'.

I have a report on file by a young psychiatric nurse who opined that my poor response to antidepressants was proof I did not have clinical depression. (I was later referred to an eminent specialist psychiatrist who diagnosed that I had moderate to severe chronic major depression.) A doctor at a psychiatric hospital gave me a wrong definition of depression in order, I presume, to convince me I was not 'really' depressed. The chief nurse at the same hospital told me how little regard he had for most of the patients because (he believed) they had made themselves psychotic through excessive use of cannabis. This fellow had probably not stopped to ask himself why people might abuse cannabis to this extent. (I have never been psychotic and I have never used cannabis.)

. . . and better ones

I am fortunate now at least in having a psychiatrist who is completely trustworthy: no 'good news', no glib assurances. He admits that I am very hard to treat. In addition I have been impressed with books on depression by people who suffer from it, particularly David Karp's *Speaking of Sadness* (1996) and Lewis Wolpert's *Malignant Sadness* (1999). Professor Karp discovered that people with chronic depression in the United States did not usually get better: they went from professional to professional, looking for 'the right one', and finally gave up! I also admire the work of people like Leanne Pethick, herself a depressive, who runs DepressioNet, a Melbourne-based online information service. I have probably learnt more about depression from people who suffer from it than from people who claim they can fix it.

What then can I say to other people with depression? First, beware of people who talk about 'beating' and 'conquering' depression. You may be fortunate in having a single bout of depression from which you make a complete and lasting recovery; but for many sufferers depression recurs or, in varying degrees, persists. It can very quickly turn living into mere burdensome existence, as can arthritis, a medical condition to which depression has been likened by some writers. So seek methods to lighten the burden. You may or may not be able to shed the burden entirely, but living with a lightened burden is better than a burdensome existence.

I know what it is like to feel suicidal for years on end. I also know how it felt to try – unsuccessfully – to prevent someone I cared about from committing suicide. Yes, you have the right to commit suicide, but doing so without trying a range of treatments for depression is a needless waste of your life. Treatment may not only help you, but it may indirectly help others, such as the people you live with or other depressives. Even if you cannot reduce your depression below intolerable levels, remember that clumsy attempts at suicide can make things worse. If you jump off a building you may still be alive at the bottom, but in a wheelchair for the rest of your life.

Seek help from professionals who are trustworthy. Professionals who give you just the 'good' news, who lie to you, or who persist in treatments that are endlessly drawn out (without any benefit to you) or that make you worse, are not worth bothering with. If your psychiatrist or psychologist behaves like a bombastic creep, trust your own judgement (of course, this is sometimes hard when you are miserable and desperate) and try to find someone else who is better!

Remember that even the best professionals are fallible. A good psychiatrist may try you on a drug that makes you worse simply because it is very hard to predict reliably how a drug will affect you. Put up with the drug for a reasonable period, then ask to stop it. A good professional will accept this; an incompetent one will say you have not tried hard or long enough, or that the drug or treatment helps 'everybody'.

If you get the chance, talk to other people who have – or have had – depression. They may help you put your own problems into perspective, and they may be able to give you helpful advice. Remember, however, that what is right for someone else may not be appropriate for you.

Finally, beware of the notion that, for some reason, you deserve to be depressed: that you must have done something to be depressed, or that depression is some sort of cosmic punishment. Nobody volunteers for depression, nor are people depressed because they are in some way unworthy of happiness. Look around, and you will occasionally find on the one hand cruel scoundrels who seem to live happy, prosperous lives without a moment of depression, and on the other hand good, kind, generous people whose lives are blighted by disability, cancer or early death. In the real world horrible and unfair things happen to good people. Having depression is a grave misfortune, but once you realise you are depressed you do not have to be fatalistic and do nothing about it.

Addendum, 2005

When my article 'Existing with Depression', was first published [December 2003], my depression had been under control for about six months. Since then I have been 'down' for a few hours on a number of occasions, but I have not been continuously and severely depressed for about nineteen months. Whether this prolonged improvement can be attributed to the medication (paroxetine) I have been taking I cannot be sure, as in the past I have had low levels of depression for about three years on two occasions when I was not taking antidepressants. I could stop taking medication, to see if this makes any difference, but the suggestion has been greeted with understandable lack of enthusiasm by my psychiatrist!

Whatever the reason for this 'remission', I find it a great relief to be able just to 'get on' with living, instead of being overshadowed by constant thoughts of death and suicide. A profound sense of loss remains, but this is reasonable enough: depression has, over the years, caused me to lose a very great deal.

When 'Existing with Depression' first appeared in print, I imagined it would attract a bit of comment, but I received more feedback (mainly by email) about this article than everything else I had published during the past forty years put together. I was particularly astonished that all the comments on the depression article were complimentary, as I was confident that one or two respondents at least would strongly disagree with me! In late 2004 a friend and neighbour told me that, while listening to the radio, she had heard a report about recent research on exercise and depression. The gist of the report was that although regular exercise could be beneficial for people with mild depression, exercise was often useless or counterproductive in cases of major depression. This seems to corroborate the point I made in my article that exercise generally made me feel worse, or even much worse, when I was depressed. (In fact wanting exercise or being able to enjoy it is a reliable sign that my depression levels have become very low.)

I am most grateful not only to everyone who wrote to me about the article but also for the comments and encouragement I received when writing and revising it from Leanne Pethick (DepressioNet), Maria Prendergast, Barry Williams (Editor of *The Skeptic*) and Dr Phil Wood. And I would like to thank Maria Prendergast for including it in her book.

In May 2004 another friend drew my attention to an article by Peter Farley, 'The Anatomy of Despair', in *New Scientist*. This gives an explanation for depression that I find powerfully plausible. It suggests that trauma or prolonged stress causes susceptible people to produce too much cortisol, which interferes with the ability of the hippocampus of the brain to make new nerve cells and connections and to buffer stress hormones. The theory fits the notion that depression seems to involve a mixture of genetic predisposition and environmental factors (stress), and offers an explanation of why, when they work, antidepressant drugs usually take two to three weeks to show any benefit. The theory may well need revising and enlarging, but I regard it as a marked improvement on claims that depression has, for some mysterious reason, an aetiology that is unfathomable or unknowable.

Neil Cole

Neil is a Research Fellow at the Alfred Hospital Psychiatric Research Centre. He is a former member of the Victorian Parliament and a successful playwright and author. Neil was diagnosed with bipolar mood disorder twelve years ago. The following is an extract from a long contribution he wrote reflecting on the personal difficulties and ongoing struggle in living and coping with his illness.

The symptoms of my illness are multiple and marked. They include unstoppable streams of ideas that are particularly bad at night and make it hard to sleep. I lie awake with thoughts racing so fast I can't remember them.

Libido issues are another major problem. The manic person is driven by their insatiable libido, which leads to a lack of sexual inhibition. The desire to achieve sexual satisfaction is so overwhelming that it is difficult to concentrate on anything else.

Excessive spending, or spending without regard to the consequences, is one of the most peculiar aspects of the illness. It is not just the amount of money spent but also the manner. This is coupled with a belief that there is no shortage of money, or somehow the money issue will sort itself out.

All of this comes with a sense of grandiosity, the belief that I am more important than others. I'm imbued with an elevated feeling that there is nothing that can stop me doing whatever I want. During these periods I have an abundance of energy. I often make excessive phone calls to people, pushing my wonderful ideas.

Another problem is that I can become very irritable when manic. My mind moves so fast that I talk very quickly and emphatically and it is infuriating when people disagree or misunderstand me. This is exacerbated by the overwhelming flight of ideas that I experience. At the time I believe my ideas are brilliant, original and worthy of consideration, yet afterwards they often seem ill-considered and foolhardy. Very often my brilliant ideas are ephemeral. Pursuing an idea one day as if there was no tomorrow, then not even considering it the next day makes me appear unstable and erratic.

At the time this irritability always seems justified to me – it is other people who can't keep up. The intensity of the irritability parallels my mania and is inverse to my self-control or self-monitoring. Because it can be such a destructive symptom, I now constantly monitor myself for signs of it, which of course is a fraught exercise as irritation and annoyance are inevitable features of all our lives. Not only does the bipolar person have to experience and manage irritability, they also have to deal with the worry that it may be a sign of impending relapse.

There are a number of things that are common to both my manic and depressive phases. Both phases are always preceded by poor sleep.

The difference is that in the manic phase I don't want to or feel the need to sleep, whereas when I feel low sleep seems like an impossible goal. Even when I do sleep it is never refreshing. Too often doctors consider sleep problems to be secondary to the illness and that some-how these problems will resolve once the episode has resolved. In fact, I find that aggressively dealing with the sleep problems not only short-ens the episode but lessens the distress and suffering associated with the episode. Rather than ignoring or dismissing sleep difficulties, doctors should see this symptom, for some patients at least, as an early warning sign of an approaching 'high' and an opportunity for early intervention.

The other aspect common to both phases is the role of stress. Every kind of stress – financial, family, relationship, social or occupational – can play its part in triggering an episode, either manic or depressive. I remain wary of engaging myself in stressful situations for fear of the effect it will have on my mental health. This is both an important pre-ventative strategy but it also limits what I feel I can take on, especially in work and relationships.

During a depressive episode, the symptoms can be the exact oppo-site. Once I was so overcome by inertia that all I could do was sit in a beanbag, watch television and eat chocolate. I believed that there was no point in living and had an all-prevailing sense of hopelessness. Everything lacked meaning, and despondency took over. I didn't care about my football team anymore, my job or my partner.

While depressed I can become very self-centred. My feelings of use-lessness and bleakness dominate, and the topic of conversation is always my view of the world or the state of things. Often as not, I ring people up and tell them how I am feeling. At the same time, for what-ever reason, seeing the dark side of things also means seeing other people's plight and understanding their problems. There is an increase in sensitivity to other people's problems. Part of being depressed is being able to see things other people cannot see, or to see them in a way that other people can't or don't want to.

Through all of these moods my judgement becomes flawed. Fear of being alone makes me seek out people. This is a problem because I am vulnerable and feel beholden to people whose company I need. If on top of this I'm obsessed, incapable of rational thinking and scared of loneliness I can do imprudent things.

Being prescribed lithium led to a dramatic change and I became very interested in creative writing, first comedy sketches then plays. I was able to occupy my mind with something that was interesting and fulfilling. That I could now concentrate for prolonged periods made a big difference. It is hard to explain the satisfaction in being able to sit and write and not feel the need to make a phone call, to get up and go for a walk, or to go and talk to someone.

Accepting treatment means the illness doesn't dominate my life. It is now possible to live comfortably without the all-pervasive symptoms of a mental illness. There are still times when I feel much worse than others; however, with medication I am better able to manage my moods.

The mere fact that each morning and each night I have to take medication is a reminder of the illness. However, it is a good reminder because it reminds me what a difference the medication has made to my life.

As part of my survival strategy, I do not carry credit cards and I try to tie my money up so I cannot get to it quickly. For some people it can be wise to see a financial counsellor who can suggest other ways of tying up money so that in a manic phase you don't blow away your house or superannuation. I also keep my house free of clutter so it doesn't make me anxious and annoyed and make me want to throw everything out.

Perhaps the biggest single issue in surviving bipolar disorder is recognising that it is an ongoing and chronic illness. While medications work and are getting better, they only work well if my mood swings are adequately monitored – I am not totally protected from going high. All the precautions I take are defence mechanisms against the extremes of the illness but it can still break through. If I do go high it's about recognising the signs and speaking to my psychiatrist. It is like having a work plan, or a plan of action.

I have been diagnosed for twelve years now. When my psychiatrist told me I was manic depressive I didn't know what it was. It has taken me many years to learn a lot about the illness. I've been hospitalised once for three weeks and have had bouts of both mania and depression – mostly depression. The illness isn't as pervasive as in the past but it's not going away. One learns to live with it, to survive it.

Laura Ballard

Laura is a writer who has been fighting depression for many years and is determined to beat it. After years of not responding to treatments she is currently being successfully treated with transcranial magnetic stimulation (TMS).

When I first heard of TMS my then doctor and I called it 'animal magnetism' because I could never remember its proper title and it was too hard to say anyway.

I had been profoundly depressed for ten years, wandering in a twilight zone with my life on hold, my existence comprising nothing except waiting to get better – and that wasn't happening. I tried cognitive behavioural therapy (CBT) first, then antidepressant after antidepressant, and finally ECT. I was completely unresponsive to any treatment except for a brief improvement when I first began taking venlafaxine (Effexor) that lasted two months before I plunged to the depths again.

And then came TMS. My doctor knew the psychiatrist running a research trial and I became one of the guinea pigs. The gods were smiling on me for a change because I got the active treatment and it worked. Two such simple words: 'it worked', yet I can barely begin to explain their meaning.

Depression is a bastard of an illness. In me, it strips away all capacity for emotion – both positive and negative – except that I retain the ability to grieve for all I have lost in the process. I lose connection with all that I love, so that in my heart I have no husband, child, parent, sibling, or friend. They are all lost to me. It is as if they are dead. Yet while my heart believes they are, my mind cannot accept this and so each morning I am freshly grief-stricken to discover the devastating loss that is my burden for the day.

In this world of destruction nothing remains to comfort me, for I have not just lost relationships, I have lost pleasure in everything. All the good things I am surrounded by have faded away to grey blobs, and so it is as though they, too, do not exist. The devastation is almost complete.

And yet there is still more, because in such a world, my own identity fades. With the loss of family, friends, all pleasures and all pains, I become ill-defined. Under a suffocating blanket of indifference, I have no likes and dislikes to help give me identity. Who am I? Who will I be if or when I emerge from the far side of hell? Who will I love? What things will I despise? My favourite foods – will they be as they were over a decade ago? I miss my Self, I want her back, but no, she is gone. The devastation is now complete.

The night is the worst time. There are no distractions from the pain of nothingness, no people to talk to, no jobs to do. There is only the pain. That's when the demon of suicide comes to me, urging me to escape, to come join with him in the dance of death. I fight the demon with fading strength. I sweat and tremble with the sheer effort of staying on the bed. I must stay on the bed! If I did not, I would not be able to stop myself; I would follow the demon and flee blindly through the night to the death I so desperately long for and so desperately battle against.

And then there are times when in the cold light of day I make a calm, dispassionate decision to end my existence and methodically begin to make the preparations.

Oh God, what a lonely, terrible place it is – that place where I have said goodbye to my time on this planet, that place where I have had my final conversations with my husband and sons and will never see them again, that place where I am in every possible respect utterly alone, with just a few hours of my existence remaining.

There is no overriding reason I survive my close encounters with suicide. I cannot say of anything, 'Yes – that is what got me through each time.' I just somehow make it. At times, the planning and preparation for my end serves to keep me busy and my thoughts occupied until the crisis passes and I no longer feel compelled to go through with it. Once, I remember making the decision and rushing out to buy what I needed, only to find the shop had just closed. By the following morning I'd decided to delay it for a while after all, and again the crisis passed. This is the hell from which TMS is able to retrieve me.

After an interstate move, I begin seeing a new psychiatrist. Through his competence and determined focus on winning the battle for my survival, he hauls me back into life each time I come close to death. Even when I lose all hope that I will get better, his stubborn belief that I *will* get better gives me something to cling to when I have nothing else left. He is the only person to come and meet me in that awful place that precedes suicide. And he gets me out, more than once. I owe him my life.

He starts me on a combination of antidepressants, at relatively high doses, and I have a few glorious months where the depression eases temporarily before I sink down again.

Then he arranges for me to continue to receive TMS even though it now means an interstate trip for me. And it continues to work. However, for me TMS is not 'The Answer'. It doesn't provide a complete or a permanent cure. In my case it appears to help brilliantly with the symptoms but not the root cause of depression: after twenty sessions of TMS over two weeks, I can count on being better for a further six weeks before beginning to relapse again. But it brings me back into what I recognise as my life and there's no doubt that I would not have made it this far without it. I've had five rounds of TMS therapy in the last four years.

To receive treatment I'm away from home for a fortnight in Melbourne, having two sessions each day. A session of 'rapid' TMS, which is the sort I get, consists of sitting back in a comfy armchair and having a figure-eight-shaped electrical coil placed in light contact with a strategic part of my skull (left prefrontal cortex for the techos). Current is passed through the coil at ten pulses per second, for five seconds, then there's a rest. This happens up to thirty times during a session. I experience intense discomfort during each burst of stimulation, and gradually over the two weeks, I acquire a colossal headache, even as the depression lifts. I understand that the discomfort and headaches are a little unusual – most people don't experience this when receiving TMS.

Anyway, the electric current in the coil induces a narrow cone-shaped magnetic field pointing downwards from the coil. This magnetic field is able to pass harmlessly through the skull and into the brain below. The electric current being switched on and off causes the magnetic field to be switched on and off, and this in turn generates an electrical field right in the part of the brain that needs to be targeted without affecting other parts of the brain.

As to why this works I'm not sure. I'm not a psychiatrist or biochemist or whatever other sort of 'ist' you might need to be to understand it all. Neurotransmitter activity levels, receptor sites and hippocampal neurogenesis all appear, among other things, to be compromised in depressed people. Perhaps TMS tackles one or more of these. The changing electrical field inside the brain might stimulate neurotransmitters, making them more active or active for longer. It may address the differential in neurotransmitter activity levels between the left and right side of the prefrontal cortex (in a depressed brain, activity tends to be lower on the left side). Or it might be related to some sort of 'improvement' of neurotransmitter receptor sites, or it might be setting in train the processes that lead to increased neurogenesis – the creation of new brain cells, particularly in the hippocampus. I'm not sure – I just know that somehow, TMS does miraculous things for me. It can drop my Beck Inventory score from 33 to 5 in just a couple of weeks.

I lived in Cambridge, England, for five years, and each year was overwhelmed by the advent of spring. The staggering transformation of the city during that season paints a picture of my return to health after TMS. I vividly recall my first spring there. The winter had been interminably long, dull and bleak. The college gardens had been beautiful, especially in the snow, but it was an austere beauty, painted in shades of grey. The sun rarely appeared, and when it did, it brought no warmth, just a feeble, rather sickly light. And then, imperceptibly, came changes, affecting a gradual, at first unseen, transformation that escalated until suddenly, with a shout of joy, spring banished the winter and the sun burst through.

The sky was a vivid blue. And the gardens! Oh the gardens! First there were joyous daffodils. Where there had been grey expanses of lawn were now brilliant green carpets with smiling daffodils everywhere. And then came the crocuses. Wonderful colours – purple and orange, red and pink and white. Wherever I looked, there were the same familiar garden beds, courtyards and lawns – the landscape essentially unaltered. And yet it was unrecognisably transformed, awash with colour and vibrant life. The same courtyards and pathways were no longer severe grey but gloriously alive. Window boxes proclaimed loudly Spring Is Here! Where previously the creepers' bare, twisting ropes imprisoned the ancient walls, now there was a delicate lacework of new green shoots giving life and colour to the old courtyards. And everywhere the beaming daffodils danced in the breezes and the lively crocuses smiled their joy.

Ah! Cambridge in spring! This is what my emergence from depression is like each time. And yet, although it brings such immeasurable relief, it does not make up for the greyness of the winter that is now past, nor the threat of winters to come. I must continue to search for the underlying causes of my illness and for treatments that might bring about permanent improvement. And I must hope that my strength lasts the distance.

I know that I may never have a permanent spring, and there may be many long, cold, grey winters ahead, but I also know that I must live in hope, always, of my spring.

Anne-Louise Allen

Anne-Louise is a writer and public relations consultant in her mid-fifties. She explains her battle with menopause and depression.

I'd describe myself as a person who has to work to be happy – happiness doesn't seem to come naturally to me as it does to others. So perhaps I'm prone to depression if the circumstances present themselves. There are three instances I'll outline for you.

In 1987 I felt my life crowding in on me. I'd started my own business two years earlier, was completely overworking, not taking care of myself physically, emotionally or mentally, and just felt as if I couldn't keep going like this. After talking to my doctor, I took up yoga, meditation, cut out caffeine, started eating properly and taking better care of myself. I felt a lot better, but after a year I still felt there were things I needed to resolve about myself and the relationship I was in at the time.

I don't think I was depressed at this point. I think this was more of a midlife crisis, clichéd though that may sound. My doctor sent me to a counsellor, and once I'd sorted through personal issues I felt a great deal better. I eventually got out of the relationship in 1992, which was the best thing for me. I began sleeping badly – whether this was as a result of feeling very emotionally unsettled or a peri-menopausal side-effect, I don't know. I was certainly not depressed about getting out of the relationship – overjoyed would be a better description!

In 1995 I entered menopause and experienced very bad hot flushes, insomnia and the return of my childhood asthma. I began hormone replacement therapy (HRT). I don't believe, however, that I was depressed at this stage.

In 1997 I broke up with a man I'd been seeing for two years. I was rather heartbroken. A very close girlfriend of mine was dying of cancer at the time, and finally passed away after a sixteen-month fight. I was sleeping extremely badly as a result of all of this, and possibly from menopausal side-effects, and finally went on antidepressants for over a year. After I stopped taking them I was fine for some time, except for a low when I turned fifty in 1999. But I got over that too.

Then in 2002 I went through a dreadful period of depression, anxiety and insomnia. I went back to my counsellor. She felt this was related to menopause, but we dealt with a number of issues, including my having to put down my two seventeen-year-old cats within three months of each other. And around this time I was finishing a relationship with a man who was, ironically, very depressed and ultimately had a nervous breakdown.

When I look back, this was a very unhappy time but didn't seem bad enough to pitch me into the black hole in which I found myself from January to August 2002. I now give more credence to the comments that my doctor and counsellor often made, for they believed this was menopause-related. (I checked the Internet – peri-menopause can take place from two to fifteen years before menopause. I have now been menopausal for eight years, and still suffer hot flushes and persistent bleeding if I go off HRT).

I did not want to go on antidepressants at this stage, because I find they do fog up my brain and reduce my mental agility. I worked with my counsellor, my yoga teacher, took up reiki and tried all manner of natural remedies (beware the naturopath who tells you they can fix depression, anxiety, hot flushes and insomnia with herbs – these failed spectacularly on all four counts!), but by July things were so bad I knew I couldn't continue.

I was having terrible anxiety attacks, was not sleeping, could hardly get myself on a plane to Sydney for a business meeting and felt I was only just hanging on to the structure of my life by a slim thread. In July I was prescribed antidepressants by a psychiatrist who had been recommended to me by a friend. Even thought this doctor was respected the drug was totally wrong for me, and I ended up taking the antidepressant for depression, sleeping pills for insomnia, and tranquillisers for anxiety. What little fight I had left in me said, 'This is wrong, wrong, wrong,' so I ditched the psychiatrist and his medication and went back to my GP who put me on another antidepressant.

Within a week I was feeling much better, much calmer. After two or three weeks I was sleeping better and the anxiety attacks had disappeared. I can only say that if you have a doctor you trust, and who knows you, get them to prescribe an antidepressant rather than going to a psychiatrist who does not know you and may get it totally wrong. I was told by the psychiatrist that I might need ECT (electroconvulsive therapy), a prospect that horrified me and that proved totally unnecessary once my GP prescribed an appropriate antidepressant.

An antidepressant can take two or three weeks to kick in properly. That's a long wait when you are feeling like hell on wheels. If, after a week or two, you have deteriorated or you just feel the medication is not right for you, talk to your doctor.

I have stayed on the antidepressant since August 2002 because I do not feel confident about going off it. I'd been back to the counsellor to talk through things, and she told me she really did not feel there was anything more that I needed to resolve. Like my doctor, she said she felt that my depression was menopause-related.

By April 2003 I felt I was slipping back into another emotional black hole, but could not identify any cause. It was a struggle to get out of bed in the morning. I often thought, 'What's the point in all this? If this is life,

I don't want the prospect of this going on endlessly into the future.' Often I only got up because my two new cats needed feeding and I knew I had to go to work. I'm a very involved person: I help run a group for single professionals and attend Monday-night drinks every week; I do a weekly yoga class and have dinner afterwards with a friend; I have a Melbourne Symphony Orchestra subscription; I have joined a book group; I ski; I have enrolled in tai chi; and I love reading, my garden, and my friends – but none of this was bringing me any joy.

I finally rang my doctor, before Easter, and said, 'Should my life be a continual struggle to be happy? Because that's what it is and I'm really, really sick of trying to talk myself up every day.' She said that no, life should not be a continual struggle. She told me that sometimes anti-depressants could lose their effectiveness, and so she changed mine. At the time, I'd been bleeding on and off for a month, presumably because of menopause. She organised for an ultrasound to check if anything else may have been the cause. The result was negative. So I began a mega dose of progesterone, thinking that if this was meno-pause, I'd rather be a bloke any day.

Once again she said that the depression could be menopause-related, so I got on the Internet, keyed in 'menopause and depression' and could have drowned in the number of articles on this topic. I finally began to realise that perhaps this depression was not my 'fault' (it's very easy to beat yourself up when you are depressed, and say you are not doing enough to get yourself out of it), and that endless counselling and positive thinking were not actually going to cure it if it was a chemical imbalance in my brain linked to menopause. I'm not copping out of taking responsibility for my own mental health, and I truly believe I have made a huge personal and very persistent effort, but if your brain chemicals are out of whack you simply may need some chemical intervention. Let's face it – I'm so involved in life, would I really want to live in that sort of state if I had a choice?

After three weeks on the new antidepressants, I woke up one morn-ing feeling happy and positive with energy and enthusiasm to get into the day. I truly could not believe it. I could not remember the last time I felt like that. It was a gem, a treasure, and I wanted more of it. This was about two or three weeks ago. I've slipped a bit when I've got overtired from too many social activities or when I've been under pressure, but I can say now that I feel either neutral, happy or very happy most of the time. The only time I was really down was the day I started to bleed again – it was just like the weepy, PMT feelings you get when you are menstruating. So clearly the HRT is not working properly, and I still need to address that.

I can only attribute this huge change in mood and outlook on life to the antidepressants. It's nothing to do with counselling, and it's nothing to do with attitude change, because I have done so much of both for so long. I do find the antidepressants affect my clarity of thought, and my memory is pretty poor right now – but it is well known that concentration and memory can be affected by menopause, so I can't actually say what's really causing it.

What I can say is that, for me, I would much rather be on antidepressants than not be on them. Right now, they're the difference between me feeling happily engaged in life – positive, enthusiastic and looking for challenges – and feeling like I am at the bottom of a black hole and that there really is no point in my existence.

Maggie Fitzherbert

Maggie has worked in education and libraries. She likes cycling and underwater photography. She is writing a book about a lost uncle.

The Change didn't come upon me till a year after I stopped bleeding. I thought it wasn't going to happen to me, that it only happened to women of my mother's generation.

I remember the day my mother disappeared. She went into another place, another zone, just sitting on the lime-green chair stroking a kitten, not recognising any of us. She refused to undress to go to bed, so I put her to bed in her corsets. After ringing the doctor I biked home, sobbing. She was in the psych ward at the hospital for six months. Nobody called it menopause, there was no HRT, no herbal remedies, no advice or therapy. There was no support at all. It was the sixties, in a small Australian city. For some reason only my father was allowed to visit her. 'It's like she's gone barmy,' he said.

A psychiatrist did try to administer 'family therapy' when she came home. He sat there not saying a word while we floundered in our ignorance and pain. 'I'm not paying any more for this,' Dad said.

The new language of the body . . . feminist theory and politics . . . advanced medical knowledge . . . women doctors . . . It wasn't going to happen to me: it hadn't happened to my friend, another woman of my generation. She'd 'sailed through it'. So when I started falling over, flushing, forgetting what happened yesterday, crying, floating out of my body, saying things I didn't believe, making bad decisions, having nightmares and anxiety attacks, the first thing I learnt was that genetics are powerful. I was my mother.

I have to say that I was working in a very stressful job at the time, that I was worn out from it, that hormonal changes had crept up and lurched me into a series of fatal attractions at work – an appalling yet unstoppable leap into unwanted fantasy. This was not acted on, but lateral damage in my life was huge. I could not stop talking about my feelings. Friends deserted me or admonished me for not keeping my fantasies to myself.

Depression set in. I went to the doctor. She put me on HRT against my better judgement. After three months the depression got worse. I thought it was because I was being harassed at work. Maybe it was. I became paranoid and freaked out totally. I stayed home for a week, catatonic on the couch. I went to a shrink, who put me on Prozac, again against my better judgement. My health was deteriorating but the Prozac did seem to help the depression. I stuck out the workplace for another nine months (a big mistake). During this time I developed intestinal polyps wending their way towards cancer.

Waking in fright . . . hallucinations . . . I had managed to distance myself from the unwanted Fatal Attractions but not my guilt in having them. And The Change had me in its claws, was pushing me down, from a fabulous apartment with views to a dirty and dangerous back alley. Disoriented, my whole life was just a mess. Me lost, everyone else a success story.

On sick leave I had lots of time to think. But who was I? What was me? What was menopause? What are drugs? What were these green flashes appearing in front of my eyes? These terrible nightmares? This emptiness?

Family deaths added to the stress. Discombobulated, exhausted, confused, I decided to go cold turkey on the Prozac and phase in a herbal remedy, St John's wort. Suddenly, death came close. Every morning I woke to a huge vacancy I cannot describe. I had never experienced anything like it before. To get up was to live, just, but why? In my early twenties I had suffered depression in London, but it hadn't been like this, like all the chemicals in my brain had changed. I was a junkie without the pleasure.

I read somewhere that too much progesterone in HRT can have deleterious effects. The doctor changed my prescription. Slight improvement but still dead every morning, feeling like shit all day. I knew I couldn't live like this much longer. I had never been suicidal before, although I had been through periods of depression. Now I was suicidal.

On a visit home to see my mother I stayed with a friend who is a marine biologist. During a conversation he happened to mention that St John's wort is a very powerful drug when combined with other drugs.

I went off HRT, too scared of the depression to stop St John's wort. The change, in a few days, was miraculous. The chemical 'death' disappeared. I was still worn out, confused, suffering the green flashes (I still have them occasionally, five years later) and unhappy. But not in a vacuous terror zone. After a while I stopped taking St John's wort too. My depression is now at a very low level and I'm almost back to being myself. Except for the gap in my mind – the lost years – and the occasional hallucination. I fear the long-term damage and struggle to find a place in the world again.

After I went off all the medication a period of intense anger set in – anger with the medical profession's inability to look after me, with philosophers, spin doctors, parents, colleagues, the government, friends, even ex-lovers. Well, anyone and everything was to blame. I had lost so much time, was so frustrated, so far behind in everything I wanted to do, and so poor. Why hadn't someone told me that you can't eat cheese, aubergine, yeast products, preserved and canned meats, sour cream, pickled fish, soy sauce, or drink wine or beer while taking St John's wort? What did I eat all that year?

Why hadn't I been told that some herbals react badly with some foods? My poor, beautiful partner copped it. But she coped. I coped. We got through it, but only just. She's going through her changes now. Less severe than mine. But I owe her one. Looking after each other, we stay out of the psych ward. A bit mad today – that's okay.

It was only when I stopped trying to find a way out and just accepted the whole mess as mine that things got better. I reached a plateau. Symptoms faded away. Words stopped falling out of my mouth like lumps of stale cake. Mountains returned from the virtual world and became real. I could climb them if I wanted, or just keep walking. I walked and walked. I stopped trying to get back the things I'd lost, the things I should have done, said or been. Peace at last. Boredom too. But that's okay for now.

Nevertheless, The Change is real. That's the moral of this story: my menopause was worse than adolescence but it didn't have to be so bad.

I'd like to think that telling all this might help other women get through their menopause without double trouble. But you can lose your ability to judge what's happening. One thing leads to another and each descent into the netherworld adds to your feelings of incompetence, failure or loss. So it's best to deal with things as they come up. Get away from the unhappy workplace *now*, from the strange new drugged sensation *now*, from the unsatisfactory doctor, therapist or psychiatrist *now*, from that absurd object of desire – you don't really want him, do you? – *now*!

There are still questions I will never be able to answer. The best I can suggest is to be careful with medication. Mixing diagnoses, health practitioners and medications can get you so confused you can no longer think clearly.

I've heard that weight-lifting is good for depression, but I haven't tried it. I've never heard of anyone having a bad reaction to Bach remedies, and a friend of mine has recently had very good results for her menopausal depression with an over-the-counter preparation called SAMe, taken with vitamin B12 in a product called Mood Lift, which you can buy from a chemist or health shop. She says it's been around since 1950. It's expensive, but since taking one a day my friend has stopped crying all the time.

My mother got better. She lived till eighty-nine. So knowing the power of genetic inheritance, I might live that long too. I'm working again, thinking, accepting my limitations, figuring out how to live with my mistakes. Relativity is vast, good and bad luck are history.

We who write in this book are luckier than the last generation of women, and are working to make it even luckier to be born in the next, when dealing with menopause and depression will be common knowledge. I don't know where I would be without my partner – her love, her anger, her tough mind. Insist. Persist. Take control.

CHAPTER EIGHT

THE TOLL OF DEPRESSION ON FAMILY AND FRIENDS

As we know depression not only affects the sufferer, it has a direct impact on his or her friends, family and colleagues. The following stories are from people whose lives have been affected by other people's depression.

Alice Martin

Alice, aged thirty-seven, is married to Scott, aged forty-two, who has suffered from severe depression for about five years. They have three children aged between five and eleven. Alice is a family therapist specialising in relationship problems. She says it is ironic that while she helps others with emotional problems and family dysfunction she is unable to help her own husband. His depression has caused emotional and communication problems between them. Alice has worked hard to develop techniques that help her deal with the strain of living with a depressed person. She wants to support her husband and help him through the hard times but is also aware that she must try and meet her own needs to remain emotionally independent and an effective and loving parent.

Scott had a very difficult and complex childhood and maybe this is the reason he suddenly developed depression when he was about thirty-seven years old. He had started to brood about his childhood and talk about the past, which was something he had never done before. He was loved as a child but the family had some very difficult times. His mother had a number of nervous breakdowns and this impacted on the children. Scott's brother was killed in a car accident and it was after this that Scott developed depressive symptoms. At first I thought it was a normal grief reaction and that he would get through it, but instead of getting over it he gradually got worse.

He was motivated to help himself, even when he was feeling very low. He had a great therapist who seemed to have the right approach for Scott's needs. He did seem to be responding quite well, but then something happened to set him back and he has not recovered. He was made redundant and this was a huge blow. He seemed to lose all confidence in himself and was desperately upset about our financial situation.

Fortunately I was working full time (our last child had just commenced school) and I thought Scott would get another job fairly quickly as he is a very skilled motor mechanic. Time passed and he did not look for another job. He said he was just too depressed to apply for anything.

It was at this point that our relationship started to suffer. He was very hard to live with. He was moody and vacillated between anger and misery. The children found it very difficult as sometimes he would basically ignore them for days on end.

For the past four years our lives have been disrupted by his depression. We live on the edge all the time, watching and waiting to see what sort of mood he is in. Scott is now on a disability pension. He is seeing a therapist and is on antidepressants but is still suffering from chronic, low-grade depression. He is not as bad as he was but he is still unmotivated and moody. I am now the bread-winner, and while he does try to help a bit around the house he is not consistent. One week he will do the cooking and help with the children, the next he will just sit in his study and look out the window.

I have to say reluctantly that my feelings for him have changed. I feel like walking out sometimes but am still hanging in there because I don't know what would happen to him if the children and I left. Sometimes I dream of a life with just myself and the children, a life where we could count on some regular stress-free times. Sometimes I feel I am going mad. Sometimes I feel so lonely because it has reached the point where we have very little to say to each other. I miss a sex life and I miss having a companion with whom I can discuss issues such as the children's education. I miss having friends around and going out to dinner as a couple. Scott simply won't connect and even when he does listen he still has an air of detached indifference.

Sometimes I think that I am suffering more than he is. I am trying to keep the home atmosphere as normal as possible for the children but it is impossible to pretend everything is okay when their father won't come out of his study for meals. The children don't like bringing their friends home because they are embarrassed about his behaviour. Sometimes he can be quite charming to their friends, at other times he will ignore them completely. The kids are acutely aware that their father is different to other dads and they don't like it. He is a bad role model, particularly for our son who yearns to have a father who is interested in doing things with him.

I crave a normal life where I could have an expectation of some happiness, and there are times when I feel desperate. Scott's depression is impacting on all of us. I have taken up yoga and I try and walk every morning before I go to work. If I don't exercise I feel more emotional and desperate. I find that exercise helps me keep going both emotionally and physically.

With Scott's permission I have talked to his doctor and therapist and they have both told me not to lose hope. But I've sort of lost hope for a happy future and a happy marriage. I have this deep-down feeling that Scott does not really care much for any of us, or he does not care enough to try and get better. I mean, he won't even make the effort to join me walking. He is getting fat and unfit. There are times when I nearly hate him for what he is doing to us all and yet I am deeply sad for him. Depression is a bad, bad place to be and our family is all affected by it. I am terrified I may become depressed myself.

Peter Lewis

Peter is a forty-six-year-old self-employed plumber with a successful business in a rural township. His wife suffers from severe chronic depression and he is extremely concerned for her wellbeing and that of their only child.

We have been married for twelve years and looking back I think Jennifer was prone to depression right from the beginning. I remember noticing that she was withdrawn even when we were dating. She could be very happy and funny but she could also be very quiet. I remember thinking that she was a bit moody but it was not an issue then.

Her moodiness – in other words, her depression – is a huge issue now and it's making life very, very hard. She seemed to go into a terrible slump after our son was born eight years ago. If it had not been for her mother and my mother I could not have kept working. Jennifer was incapable of looking after the baby and stayed in bed weeping for months. Our doctors thought it was severe postnatal depression and I was told that her moods would lift in time. She did briefly improve but for the past six years she has been in a constant depressed state. Some days she seemed to be a bit better, and I used to hope that she was improving, but then she would slump again.

Her life is awful for her and it is sheer bloody hell for me and my kid. She does not seem to respond to any medication or therapy. She has been on all sorts of medication including anti-psychotic drugs, and nothing seems to be able to make a lasting impression. Our local GP is fantastic and has been incredibly emotionally supportive to all of us. He often phones me just to see how I am. Just knowing he is there to listen is a help, because there are times when I get pretty low myself because of all the pressure and stress.

Jennifer has been to Sydney for hospitalisation and has even had shock treatment. She knows she is depressed and says it is a terrible place to be. We don't function as a normal family because Jennifer does not want to go out and meet people. She can't even face the school fete or sports day and this used to be very upsetting for our boy. Now he is used to it and does not expect his mum to be around. One of her greatest sorrows is that she wanted to have more children but there is no way I am going to have another child under the circumstances. I had a vasectomy and that upset my parents, who wanted more grandchildren, and Jennifer was quite distraught. But I know that neither Jennifer nor myself could cope with another child. I live with this constant worry that she will kill herself, and our boy will be the first to find her. She talks about death, saying it has to be preferable to her life. On her really bad days I often ring every hour and rush home during jobs to check on her. I have this constant fear that one day I will come home and she will be dead, unless we can find a miracle drug. I have my son collected from school every day by another mother who walks him home because I don't want him to go home and find her dead or asleep in bed.

That is where my wife spends most of her time – in bed. I do all the cooking and shopping. It is tragic because there are days when she feels a little better and I come home and she has made an effort to get dressed and do something in the house. I broke down a few weeks ago because she had picked some flowers and put them on my bedside table. It was like a sign of life and it was a gesture of love. I just howled in front of Jennifer and our son. It could be so different if she could get on top of her illness. She is smart and pretty and it breaks my heart to see her suffering so much. I've told her to get a job if she wants and we can get a cleaner in to do the domestics, but she is not interested in working. I have tried to get her to join groups and take up exercise but absolutely nothing interests her. This is the hardest part, I think, watching someone you love just existing rather than living.

I go bushwalking once a month when my parents look after my son and Jennifer's mother stays over to look after her. All our parents are getting old and frail and I don't know what I will do when they can no longer help. They have all been amazingly supportive.

My worst moment was only a few days ago when my son, in quite an offhand manner, asked me if I would remarry when his mum dies. I was devastated to realise that he too thinks she might suicide one day. I have never discussed this with him as I don't think a child of his age should have to live with such a fear. It really is terrible that he lives with such a shadow over him. I really feel for the poor little chap, as he would love to have a mum who was capable of taking part in family life. I have to say that I cannot quite believe that life can be so tough. Unless Jennifer gets better, I suppose life will be just more of the same. I guess I have given up hope and that's not a good thing.

Anita Berman

Anita is a fifty-five-year-old graphic designer. Her husband, Alan, is a medical scientist in his late fifties. They have two adult children and agree they had a particularly happy and carefree life until about three years ago when Alan started having anxiety attacks. He subsequently developed severe depression. Alan is unable to identify a reason for his initial anxiety. The impact of his mental illness on their relationship and his physical health and career has been dramatic. Anita is very angry that Alan talks about hating his life while refusing to follow his doctor's advice.

I believe that the man I have been in love with for thirty years is still there, but I must confess there are moments when I wonder if he will ever reappear. I am normally not a particularly angry person but currently I am very angry about the havoc caused by this horrible illness called depression. Both of us feel very frustrated that we do not know why Alan suddenly became anxious and depressed and in such a big way.

Our doctor says that it can happen like that. It can just appear for no apparent reason. I'm not sure I agree with this. Even if this depression were purely chemically based I would like to know what caused the chemical changes. I mean, how can something as severe as clinical depression just 'happen'? As far as we know we have no family history of depression and we certainly have no previous experience in coping with it.

Alan has been prescribed antidepressants but does not take them all the time. As a scientist he should know that he cannot mess around with his medication. I think it is because he believes that to be on long-term medication is a sign of weakness. He has lied to me about taking his medication and this has caused me a lot of pain. We had always been very frank and honest with each other in the past.

I find his attitude very upsetting as his depression is not improving and he does not seem motivated enough to bite the bullet and do something about it. He only rarely goes to work and he can get away with this because he is a consultant to a company who just love him and who are prepared to put up with his erratic appearances. His general health is not good. He has a lot more physical ailments than before he became depressed. He says he cannot imagine living the rest of his life feeling so awful and says he would rather be dead. But he still does nothing!

What the hell am I meant to say or do when he speaks like this? I really thought I was going mad until I went to a new GP. This doctor was sympathetic to me. This was the first time I received any support. Mostly it is Alan who gets the sympathy vote. This doctor gave me permission to feel comfortable expressing my feelings about the situation. My feelings are not benign.

I am having a really hard time recognising that it is ultimately up to Alan to take responsibility for his illness. I will not and do not feel guilty. I do not feel selfish. I am not a hard bitch. But I will not allow Alan's depression to ruin my life. I will be supportive but I will not be consumed. I have started to organise pleasurable activities outside the time I spend with Alan. I go out with friends and have had a few weekends away. I have told Alan I still love him but unless he is prepared to help himself he should not assume that I will remain in the marriage.

What I have said may sound awful but I don't think it is right that life should be a living hell because your partner is not prepared to tackle an illness that could probably improve dramatically with proper treatment.

I am lucky that I have the type of personality that is not overwhelmed by this ongoing and very emotionally destructive situation. I have, thank God, always been a fairly independent person and know how to utilise options that are available to me. I have a friend who is in a very similar situation to mine and yet she is going under. She has always been very passive and quiet and would do little without her husband. Now that he is suffering from depression she has no life of her own at all. She cannot imagine going out alone or initiating activities for herself.

I am about to start some joint therapy with Alan in the hope that he will realise the importance of treatment. It has taken some time to get him to agree to this but at least it is a start. I actually told him I would leave unless he acted. It was the bombshell he needed to make a move in the right direction. You never know, we might even have a sex life again in the future. I want the old Alan back.

Joy's story

Joy is a fifty-three-year-old Aboriginal woman who lives in Darwin with five of her six children. She is actively involved in trying to help local Aboriginal children and youths combat some of the family and social problems that are common in the community. Joy left school when she was sixteen but went on to study as an adult, and acquired strong administrative skills. Two of her children suffer from depression, as do many of their friends.

Compared to the problems in some of the remote communities in the Northern Territory most of the kids around here have more opportunity. However, I want to be honest and say that there is real social dysfunction within many Aboriginal communities. I know there are big problems in white families, but many Aboriginal communities are terrible places to live. Some have absolutely no facilities and there is nothing for the kids to do.

My husband and I decided early on to try and give our kids the best opportunities, and when they were young we moved to Sydney. In retrospect this was a mistake as the two eldest got into a bad crowd and started drinking and smoking and staying out at night. Both these kids have now been diagnosed with severe depression. They are now nineteen and twenty and are living at home with me.

The depression hit them roughly around the same time. It was about three years ago and my marriage was breaking up. I know this upset all the kids but the two eldest took it very hard. Both had previously seemed interested in getting a qualification from school but suddenly they just lost interest in their work and started playing up badly. I decided to come back to Darwin as I had more family support and I basically thought it a better environment than Redfern for the kids. My husband stayed behind in Sydney. The kids see him a few times a year and he does all he can to help them. He is a good man but we had grown apart.

For the last few years I have tried everything to get my boys well again. The medical support here has been quite good but the boys don't like taking antidepressants. They start them and then stop and then start again. They won't see a counsellor, even though the doctor wants them to. Both are unemployed and stay in bed most days until well into the afternoon. It is really bad for the other kids to see their brothers in this state.

They blame me, the family, the government and the doctor for their miserable lives. I know clinical depression is a terrible illness but I so wish the boys could have some sense of hope. They just don't see any future for themselves. Our worst time was when the eldest tried to kill himself last year. We got him to hospital in time but it was a terrible thing for us all.

I have an okay house and enough income and the other kids are doing well at school. We could be happy but the two boys make all our lives miserable. Our doctor is a caring man and tries to help and so do my extended family, but until the boys can try and meet us maybe even quarter of the way I cannot see how their lives will improve. We live with an ongoing sense of hopelessness.

The worst thing about depression is that hopelessness. When the boys do sometimes talk about how they feel they talk about feeling hopeless. I was so desperate to get all my kids a good education because I think education gives you hope. I tell them they can still get an education but they don't listen to me. The doctor tells me all sorts of people get depression, even people with good jobs and plenty of money.

Sometimes the feeling of depression in our house is hard to bear. It is a sickness that has taken over our whole family. We all suffer because of depression.

Janie Hughes

Janie's twenty-year-old daughter committed suicide three years ago. Her daugher was an academically brilliant student who seemed to be enjoying life until depression hit. Her parents, siblings and friends are still struggling to come to terms with her death.

Is it mainly psychiatric illness that makes people so desperate that they kill themselves? Are the symptoms of depression so awful and so severe that the sufferer feels there is no way out except death? Till I die myself I will question whether I could have done more for my daughter. These feelings of guilt, anger and remorse never leave me. In our case depression became a silent killer. Our family will be forever affected by what happened.

For the two years before my daughter died I knew that there was something wrong and I felt I was going mad, trying to get into a brain that simply refused to allow me access. On the surface she looked the same, but the girl we knew and loved for twenty years was gone. Her behaviour slowly changed. She became introverted and secretive. Until then we had enjoyed a very close and loving relationship and I was very upset when she started to withdraw from me. She denied anything was wrong and seemed to resent me asking. She put on weight and did openly say that this was upsetting. That was about the only issue that she did admit was making her unhappy. Previously she had been slim and played sport on a regular basis.

She stopped participating in any form of exercise and spent most of her time in her room or stayed on her own at a friend's beach house. She told my husband that she was thinking about dropping her law course as she was bored and had decided she did not want to be a lawyer. She still attended some lectures but we all noticed that she was not studying. Previously she had been an outstanding student and was topping her year. At no time did we sense that she felt under any pressure regarding her course.

I feel there are still so many unanswered questions about depression.

Why did a truly happy and popular girl suddenly get depressed? We have gone over that last year of her life so many times and we still cannot find a reason why. She had a great boyfriend who was very supportive and who continued to love her after she became so moody and reclusive. She had absolutely refused to go to a doctor and we feel very neglectful in hindsight that we did not confront her over this and make her see a doctor or a counsellor. We suggested many times that she seek medical help but she ignored us. It is hard, as every parent knows, to make a young person do something they don't want to do. I am unable to go into the details of her death because I will break down, but she killed herself when we were away for the weekend and she knew she would be alone. She left us a note saying she loved us and we were all better off without her.

As a family we are devastated. I feel I will never be able to be happy again. I cannot believe that none of us picked up the signs that she was so ill. We knew she was depressed or very troubled but we never in our wildest dreams thought she was considering suicide. I also feel guilt that my two other children are having to deal with such pain and the ongoing sadness of my husband and myself. We have decided that some family therapy may help us collectively deal with our grief and our GP is going to arrange this. None of us are functioning too well.

Claude Lefroy

Claude, a fifty-eight-year-old academic, is married and has three sons. The middle son, who is in his late thirties, came back home to live with his parents after being diagnosed with severe depression.

All our children had left home and all seemed to be enjoying what they were doing professionally. They all had partners and all were happy – or so it seemed.

My wife and I were planning to go overseas on an extended holiday. I had some long-overdue leave and my wife who is a GP had arranged a locum for three months. We were two weeks away from leaving for

Europe when my eldest son rang us and said his brother was in real trouble. My first thought was that he must have run foul of the law in some way. This son had always been less conservative than his brothers and I knew that he occasionally used marijuana.

My eldest son soon explained the problem. Ostensibly without much warning or indication my middle son had gone into a severely depressed emotional state. His partner, a journalist, was overseas and my son had rung his brother in desperation. Thankfully we all live in the same city and my wife and I were able to drive straight over. We were totally shocked by our son's emotional and physical condition. He looked absolutely exhausted and unkempt. We had seen him only about two weeks before and he seemed fine. He later told us that he thought he was spiralling into some sort of emotional crisis but was managing to keep it to himself. My wife, who has some experience with depression through her clinic, did comment that she thought he seemed a bit agitated but there was nothing in his behaviour that made us unduly worried.

We were amazed when he actually accepted our suggestion to come home with us for the night. He is normally very independent and has not lived at home for years.

I was aware that he was pacing the floor most of the night and in the morning he looked and sounded worse. He was lethargic but nervy and very defensive. It was a Saturday morning so we suggested he stay for the weekend and let us look after him while he got over his 'virus'. He agreed. He spent most of the weekend in bed and had no desire to communicate with any of us.

My wife told me on Sunday evening that she thought he was suffering from depression. I was amazed, as he had always been a very optimistic and cheerful young man and there seemed to be no obvious reason why he should have been depressed.

Well, now we know there does not have to be an obvious reason. I did wonder at the time whether he was having relationship trouble. He is gay and his live-in partner is away quite a bit with his job. Our other sons assured us that there was no problem with the relationship. They said our son was very happy with his partner and it was a mutually loving relationship. By this time our sick son was hardly speaking. He just slept, or sat on a sofa looking out the window.

There was no way he was capable for work on Monday and we phoned his employers and told them we thought he'd be off work for a week. This was okay with them as long as he got a doctor's certificate. My wife has always had a policy not to treat family members unless it was an emergency and so told our son she wanted to take him to her clinic for a check-up with a colleague. He overreacted badly and told us he was furious we had rung his boss and that he did not need to see a doctor. However, he offered no alternatives and went back to bed. He did not suggest going back home or to work. It was like life outside our spare bedroom had lost all relevance.

The upshot of all this is that our son was diagnosed as severely depressed. He still is, though there are some signs of improvement. He was so bad that he has not been back to work or gone home for nearly two months. He finally agreed to see a doctor when my wife told him that she was going out of her mind with worry. He has expressed concern about causing us such worry and trouble but he can also be verbally rather aggressive, particularly at night. It certainly is devastating to see someone just give up on their life. He is having regular therapy, which he says is a total waste of time as he dislikes the therapist (who, he says, is smug). He is also on medication, the doses of which have been changed two or three times because there was negligible improvement.

Thank God there seems to have been improvement in the past few weeks. He has got dressed and joined us for a few meals and there are glimpses of the old self. His partner has been terrific and has stayed with us a number of nights and been supportive to us all. Even his partner's parents whom we did not know have visited. We have been touched and quite surprised at the support and understanding of friends. We have also been surprised at the number of friends who say they have been depressed or have family or other friends with depression.

We have cancelled our trip and instead of going back to work my wife has decided to stay home and look after our son. I think her dedication and love for him has been very beneficial in his recovery, slow though it is. He has always been close to me but has become much closer to his mother since he moved back home. In fact he seems to avoid me and this is upsetting. I have made a point of telling him I am there for him, but I get very little feedback or response.

It has been a very distressing time and I have to say I look forward to the day when he is ready to move back to his own home. I don't think it is ideal for any of us having an adult son living in the house. I have tried to suggest a move home on a few occasions as I think it would be best for him to start taking some control of his life again, but I get very cool looks from my wife and a vacant look from my son. I imagine that if he keeps on improving he will want to go home, but as he has shown no indication of wanting to reclaim his own life he still has a long way to go in the recovery process.

There are slight tensions in my relationship with my wife. She is completely tied up with our son and our normal social and domestic life has changed. We have not been out together since our son came home because she does not want to leave him, even when he has friends visiting or his partner is staying over.

I worry that her medical training may have alerted her to something about his depression that she is not telling me. I know that she has asked him not to smoke marijuana while he is on antidepressants. I have asked if the smoking could have caused the depression and she said she doubted it because he smoked very little. She just thinks it prudent to keep off marijuana while on medication. Still I worry about him nearly all the time. I have looked up marijuana on the Internet and its possible role in psychosis and emotional disturbances is not reassuring. I wonder whether he has smoked more than he has told us about, or whether he was on other drugs. I find his passivity and lack of engagement very concerning.

Depression is a frightening and complex illness and who knows if we will ever get to the bottom of why our son has it so badly. He has a good life and everything going for him. I really don't understand the situation at all and I don't think he does either.

Natalie Andrews

Natalie is a thirty-seven-year-old public relations consultant who suffered severe postnatal depression for some months.

I could not believe how terrible I felt, especially as I had been so ecstatic about having a baby and both my husband and myself were really ready for this new addition to the family. This was a planned child and every-thing went to plan – even the birth was not too bad. The baby was perfect, we were thrilled and our families were supportive. Both my husband and I cried tears of joy. We were over the moon. That is until I had been home for a few days. One day I could not stop crying. I felt terrible and ridden with guilt. What had I to cry about?

We did not know it but we were about to embark on three months of hell. If it had not been for the amazing support of my husband, his mother and my mother's friend, I believe I would have killed myself. I was completely exhausted, unable to express love and I felt personally unlovable. Our whole world seemed to have crashed.

The baby had severe reflux and colic and cried for hours on end. I was sleep deprived and desperate. I had looked forward to having a baby but it had turned into a nightmare for both my husband and myself. I was ratty and irritable. My husband was upset and worried at my inability to cope. He tried to be supportive but I was not in the mood to be helped. I will never forget the night I screamed at him and told him I was sick of him and the baby. He was devastated and hurt. We went through a few horrible weeks barely speaking to each other. I cried most of the day and found myself really resenting the baby. This was the baby I had dreamt about and longed for and yet here I was resenting this dear little girl. I hated seeing her suffer with the colic and would be desperate for her to stop crying. Sometimes I felt as if I was insane. It was a rollercoaster of emotions. The day I nearly shook her was the day I realised I was nearing breaking point. The very, very worst part was that I even thought of killing myself and the baby because I did not want her to grow up without a mother. I was truly out of my head.

I was scared of myself. I rang my mother who lived interstate and told her I was desperate. She was not able to come over as she was looking after my father who was recovering from a hip replacement, but within about ten minutes of that call, one of her friends was at my door. Mum had gone into super-organising mode. She had tried to call my husband but he was out on a building site and his mobile was switched off. She later told me she was prepared to call the police if her friend had not been available, and I respect this decision as I was a danger to myself and the baby.

I just cried and cried when Mum's friend walked in. She just took over. I was taken to a GP who had me admitted to hospital after she diagnosed severe depression. I think the word 'psychotic' was used.

I felt such a failure. My husband's mother moved in and she and my mother's friend looked after the baby between them while my husband was at work. I stopped breastfeeding and felt a double failure but also felt a sense of relief that I was away from the baby and the chaos that was my home.

It was the most scary and unhappy time of my life. For a few days I did little but sleep and cry. I was treated with medication and had some therapy once I was feeling a bit better. I was much luckier than many women because I responded quickly to the treatment and in about three weeks I felt a lot better. I was anxious to get back home and have a second chance at motherhood. My husband had some counselling with me and that was great because he then understood that he was not married to a raving mad woman. Neither of us previously knew anything about postnatal depression and it was reassuring for us to be told that it is common and most people get through it without permanent damage.

Our marriage survived my behaviour. I finally bonded with our darling baby and believe it or not we are planning to have another child. I have been told that I may have postnatal depression again as the odds are higher if you have had it previously. However, this time we will be prepared for it. Nothing could be as awful as what we went through. I realise that we were lucky to have support from family and friends. I simply do not know what I would have done if I had no one to help while I was in hospital.

CHAPTER NINE

USEFUL CONTACTS AND RESOURCES

Most public hospitals have a Crisis Assessment Team (CAT) that can respond to people in need. Lifeline will provide information on the quickest way to contact the nearest hospital, or try Telstra's Directory Assistance on 1223.

Help lines

Lifeline 131114
A twenty-four hour service for people in distress.

Lifeline Just Ask 1300 131 114
A rural mental health service, available Monday to Friday 9 a.m. to 5 p.m. EST.

Men's Help Line 1300 136 459
Particularly helpful for men in rural Australia who have fewer support systems.

Post & Antenatal Depression Association (PANDA) 1300 130 026
(freecall for Victoria only); (03) 9428 4600
info@panda.org.au
Provides telephone support, information and referral.

Recorded Information 1300 360 980
Cost of a local call from anywhere in Australia.
A twenty-four–hour telephone suicide prevention service with recorded information about depression and where to seek further help. Clear and concise advice from a clinical psychiatrist on dealing with suicidal thoughts.

SANE 1800 688 382

Advice and information, available Monday to Friday 9 a.m. to 5 p.m.

1800 187 263

Referral to support organisations that can provide counselling, legal advice, financial advice and help with other issues (available Monday to Friday 9 a.m. to 5 p.m.).

Suicide Prevention 1300 651 251

Cost of a local call from anywhere in Australia.

Web-based resources

Association of Relatives and Friends of the Mentally Ill (ARAFMI)

www.arafmi.org.au

Provides information, care, support and referral in each state and territory for people who care for the mentally ill.

Beyondblue

www.beyondblue.org.au

Beyondblue is a national, independent, nonprofit organisation that works to address issues associated with depression, anxiety and substance misuse disorders.

Black Dog Institute

www.blackdoginstitute.org.au

Provides information about depression including the latest research on diagnosis and treatment.

Blue Pages

www.bluepages.anu.edu.au

Online information about the symptoms and treatment of depression. Produced by the Centre for Mental Health Research (CMHR). Has help and resources and a bulletin board.

DepressioNet

www.depressioNet.com.au
Online information about depression. Provides bulletin boards and chat rooms where people with depression and related conditions can communicate anonymously twenty-four hours a day. You can also email (team@depressionet.com.au).

GROW National

www.grow.net.au
A community mental health organisation with groups throughout Australia, offering support for those affected by mental illness. The national office contact number is (07) 3397 6934.

Living is for Everyone (LIFE)

www.livingisforeveryone.com.au
A new website geared specifically for government agencies, nonprofit organisations and community groups working towards reducing suicide in indigenous communities. This site contains information about government mental health policies and local suicide prevention initiatives.

Mental Illness Fellowship of Australia

www.mifa.org.au
National body for the Mental Illness and Schizophrenia Fellowships, which support and represent people with mental illness and their carers. Their national office can be reached on (08) 8221 5072.

Reachout

www.reachout.com.au
Online information and support for young people who are going through tough times.

SANE

www.sane.org.au
National charity working for a better life for Australians affected by mental illness, through education, applied research and campaigning. The national office contact number is (03) 9682 5933.

REFERENCES

A major source of information for this book has been face-to-face interviews with individual psychiatrists, psychologists, medical doctors and other specialists in the mental health area, both in Australia and the United Kingdom. The World Health Organization bulletin reports were also widely sourced (www.who.int/mental_health/en/) as were journals such as the *Medical Journal of Australia* and reports from the Mental Health Research Institute.

Page 10   Asthma and depression: R D Goldney, R Ruffin, D Wilson & L Fisher 2003, 'Asthma symptoms associated with depression and lower quality of life', *Medical Journal of Australia*, vol. 178, no. 9, pp. 437–41.

Page 17   Heart disease and depression: S J Bunker et al 2003, '"Stress" and coronary heart disease: psychosocial factors', *Medical Journal of Australia*, vol. 178, no. 6, pp. 272–6.

Page 44   Ethnicity and antidepressants: C H Ng, I Schweitzer, T Norman & S Easteal 2004, 'The emerging role of pharmacogenetics: implications for clinical psychiatry', *Australian and New Zealand Journal of Psychiatry*, vol. 38, no. 7, pp 483–9.

Page 50   Deep brain stimulation study: stimulation of the frontal cortex brought about a 'striking and sustained remission' in four out of six patients suffering from clinical depression who had previously been resistant to any treatment; H Mayberg 2005, 'Deep brain stimulation for treatment-resistant depression', *Neuron*, March, vol. 45, pp. 651–60.

Page 53   St John's wort and depression: A Jorm, H Christensen, K Griffiths & B Rodgers 2002, 'Effectiveness of complementary and self-help treatments for depression', *Medical Journal of Australia*, vol. 176, no. 10 supplement, pp. 86–7.

Page 53 Omega 3 and depression: ibid., p. 93.

Page 53 Other complementary therapy surveys: G T Lewith & A Bensoussan 2004, 'Complementary and alternative medicine with a difference', *Medical Journal of Australia,* vol. 180, no. 11, pp. 585–6.

Page 54 Professor Schaefer's laughter experiments: E Foley, R Matheis, C Schaefer 2002, 'Effect of forced laughter on mood', *Psychological Reports*, vol. 90, no. 1, p. 184.

Page 59 Oxytocin reduces stress: R J Kershaw et al 2004, 'Oxytocin attenuates stress-induced c-fos MRNA expression', *Journal of Neuroscience*, vol. 24, no. 12, pp. 2974–82.

Page 74 University graduate's depression improves: G Parker & T Watkins 2002, 'Treatment-resistant depression: when antidepressant drug intolerance may indicate food intolerance', *Australian and New Zealand Journal of Psychiatry*, vol. 36, no. 2, pp. 263–5.

Page 76 Sensitivity to artificial colours and flavours: L Clarke et al 1996, 'The dietary management of food allergy and food intolerance in children and adults', *Australian Journal of Nutrition and Dietetics*, vol. 53, no. 3, pp. 89–94.

Page 77–8 English farmers and pesticides study: M Day 1998, 'Dipping into danger – fears are mounting over routine exposure to pesticides', *New Scientist*, no. 2122, p. 5.

Page 78 Triphosphates cause depression in rats: International Programme on Chemical Safety (IPCS) 1998, 'Environmental Health Criteria 209, Flame retardants: tris(chloropropyl) phosphate and tris (2-chloroethyl) phosphate', <http://www.inchem.org/documents/ehc/ehc/ehc209.htm>.

Page 78 Organophosphates: American Chemical Society (ACS) 2000, 'Chemical found in computer can cause allergy, sickness [sic]', *Science Daily*, <http://www.sciencedaily.com/releases/2000/09/000919080653.htm>.

Page 95 Nigel Sinnott's story: Peter Farley 2004, 'The anatomy of despair', *New Scientist*, no. 2445, pp. 43–5.

FURTHER READING

Aldridge, S, *Seeing Red & Feeling Blue*, Century, London, 2000.

Hassed, C, *Know Thyself*, Michelle Anderson Publishing, Melbourne, 2002.

Jamison, K, *An Unquiet Mind: A Memoir of Moods and Madness*, Alfred A. Knopf Inc., New York, 1995.

——*Night Falls Fast*, Picador, London, 2000.

Karp, D, *Speaking of Sadness*, Oxford University Press, London, 2000.

Kelly, M, *Life on a Roller-Coaster*, Simon & Schuster, Sydney, 2002.

Kramer, D, *Listening to Prozac*, Fourth Estate, London, 1994.

Orum, M, *Fairytales in Reality*, Pan Macmillan, Sydney, 1996.

Parker, G, *Dealing with Depression*, Allen & Unwin, Sydney, 2002.

Rowe, D, *The Successful Self*, Harper Collins, London, 1993.

Rzecki, C, *Surfing the Blues*, Angus & Robertson, Sydney, 1996.

Sarton, M, *Journal of a Solitude*, The Women's Press, London, 1991.

Smith, G, *Sharing the Load*, Random House, New Zealand, 1996.

Solomon, A, *The Noonday Demon*, Vintage, London, 2002.

Sontag, S, *Illness as a Metaphor*, Penguin Books, London, 1983.

Storr, A, *Churchill's Black Dog*, Harper Collins, London, 1989.

Styron, W, *Darkness Visible*, Picador, London, 1992.

Wolpert, L, *Malignant Sadness: The Anatomy of Depression*, Faber & Faber Ltd, London, 1999.

ACKNOWLEDGEMENTS

This book would not exist without the input and support of the many people who shared their personal experiences of depression with me.

I hope they all know how I value their honesty and how much their contributions have enriched this book. These people gave unstintingly of their time and spoke from their hearts. I respect them all so much. Thank you for your faith in me and helping me make a contribution to the community's understanding of depression.

I would particularly like to thank Neil Cole, Nigel Sinnott and Laura Ballard not only for their contributions but for their ongoing encouragement and support. I want to acknowledge another contributor, Peter Lewis, for his bravery.

The support and assistance I had from Leanne Pethick, the founder of DepressioNet, was invaluable as was the support from Barbara Hocking and Paul Morgan from SANE Australia.

I want to acknowledge, with gratitude, conversations and advice from Kristin Chandler, Natasha Prendergast, Maria Vandamme, Rita Erlich, Mark Parsons, Megan Carroll, Christina Fitzgerald, Helen Reynolds, Rose Cuff, Helen Long and many others. You know who you are.

Sincere thanks also to Sue Dengate for her important chapter on food and chemical intolerance.

I would like to thank the many GPs, psychologists, psychiatrists and others in the medical and mental health area who gave their time so generously. In particular I want to acknowledge the input of Dr Charles Kerr, Dr David Grounds, Dr Kath Dunne, Dr Robert Procter, Professor David Copolov, Associate Professor Paul Fitzgerald, Phil Blackwood, Professor Colin Johnstone, Dr Alice Murkies, and Professor George Fink and Ross Johnstone from the Mental Health Research Institute.

Acknowledgements

Again that staunch Penguin, Robert Sessions, maintained his faith in me, and his encouragement, commitment and belief in this book never faltered. Many thanks to my editor Miriam Cannell whose input made this a better book. She was a brick.

The love and support of my husband John Loder was sorely tested at times when I was immersed in interviewing and writing. He was my rock, particularly during the times of numerous computer disasters.

INDEX

Index

Index